KU-652-349

About the Authors

Brian Nolan is Research Professor at The Economic and Social Research Institute. He is the author of *Child Poverty in Ireland* and a joint author of *Resources, Deprivation and Poverty*, *Where Are Poor Households?*, *Women and Poverty in Ireland* and *Loading the Dice: A Study of Cumulative Disadvantage*.

Miriam M. Wiley is Research Professor and Head of the Health Policy Research Centre at The Economic and Social Research Insitute. She is the co-author of *Women and Health Care in Ireland* and co-editor of *The Irish Health System in the 21st Century*.

P/O NO:
ACCESSION NO: KHOO922
SHELFMARK: 362.109415/NoL

PRIVATE PRACTICE IN IRISH PUBLIC HOSPITALS

Brian Nolan and Miriam M. Wiley

Oak Tree Press
Dublin
in association with
The Economic and Social Research Institute

Oak Tree Press
Merrion Building
Lower Merrion Street
Dublin 2, Ireland
http://www.oaktreepress.com

© 2000 The Economic and Social Research Institute

A catalogue record of this book is
available from the British Library.

ISBN 1 86076 194-1

All rights reserved. No part of this publication may be reproduced or
transmitted in any form or by any means, including photocopying and
recording, without written permission of the publisher. Such written
permission must also be obtained before any part of this publication
is stored in a retrieval system of any nature. Requests for permission
should be directed to Oak Tree Press, Merrion Building,
Lower Merrion Street, Dublin 2, Ireland.

This study forms part of The Economic and Social Research Institute's
General Research Series, in which it is Paper No. 175. It has been
subject to the normal internal and external refereeing procedures
employed for that series and accepted for publication by the Institute,
which is not responsible for either the content or the views
expressed therein.

Printed in the Republic of Ireland by Colour Books Ltd.

Contents

Acknowledgements

In carrying out this study we have benefited greatly from discussions with a range of people working in the health services, as well as with officials in the Department of Health and Children. A list of those consulted is given in Appendix 1, and we would like to record here our appreciation for their contribution to the study, although the views expressed are of course those of the authors. We also wish to acknowledge the sterling work done by Anne Clifton, Claire Doble and colleagues in the HIPE Unit. The study also draws on the 1994 and 1997 waves of the *Living in Ireland Survey*, the Irish element of the European Community Household Panel, and Brendan Whelan, James Williams and Dorothy Watson were responsible for the survey design, data collection and database creation. We are very grateful to Colm Harmon of University College Dublin and to our colleague Richard Nestor, for allowing us to draw here on joint work being undertaken by Brian Nolan with them on cross-sectional and time-series demand for health insurance respectively. Finally, we would like to thank our ESRI colleagues Dr Tony Fahy and Professor Gerry Hughes and an anonymous external referee for very helpful comments received on earlier drafts of this study.

General Summary

Ireland's health services are a complex and sometimes confusing mixture of public and private provision and financing. This is particularly true in the crucial area of acute hospital services. Private care is received not only in private hospitals, but also in public hospitals which have private accommodation catering for the private patients of their consultant doctors. This has major implications for health insurance, since covering the cost of private care in public and private hospitals has been the main role of health insurance in Ireland.

This structure gives rise to a number of issues about efficiency and equity in delivering acute hospital services, the focus of the present study. Its aims are first to assess the extent of private practice within the public hospital sector, the characteristics of the case-mix being dealt with, and the costs associated with provision of that care. The stated intention of public policy is to move to charging the full cost of provision for such private practice in public hospitals, so the study then turns to the impact that might have on demand for health insurance. This involves an in-depth consideration of the factors underlying the demand for health insurance in Ireland. Finally, we consider the adequacy of the arrangements currently in place regarding equity of access for public patients, which involve *inter alia* the designation of beds as private versus public and the monitoring of their use.

The Institutional and Policy Context

In the mid-1980s, the Commission on Health Funding concluded that there was a major problem regarding access to public hospitals, the common perception being that those opting for private care were able to obtain admission more quickly than those using the public system and that private care was higher quality. This, the Commission felt, helped to explain the substantial take-up of health insurance in Ireland. Since that time the number with private health insurance has continued to grow and has now reached about 40 per cent of the population. This poses major challenges for a system designed for a situation where about 15 per cent of the population had health insurance and were effectively encouraged and subsidised by the state to do so, in return for limited public entitlement. As well as tax relief on health insurance premia, for many years this subsidisation took the form of charges for private patients in public hospitals which represented at most only the marginal cost of the accommodation.

From the early 1990s the situation where the top 15 per cent of the distribution had limited entitlement to public hospital care was ended, entitlement being extended to everyone (though only people with medical card cover being free of all charges). At the same time, new arrangements were set up to restrict private patients in public hospitals to private beds, and to increase policy-makers' control over the mix of public and private beds. The per-night charge for private and semi-private accommodation in public hospitals has also been increased significantly. The current level of this charge is still widely regarded as well below the cost of the resources employed in treating private patients, and the stated intention of public policy is now to move towards charging the full cost of providing private hospital care. The issue also arises as to how effectively the arrangements for access to public versus private beds are working.

Private Care in Public Hospitals

About 20 per cent of in-patient beds in acute public hospitals are currently designated as being for private patient use. A private patient in a public hospital is someone opting to avail of private consultant services, and the proportion of all bed-days spent in public hospitals accounted for by private patients rose from 18 per cent in 1995 to 21 per cent in 1997, with private pa-tients accounting for about the same proportion of day bed use.

To look in more detail at the private and public workload in public hospitals, in particular the characteristics of the case-mix involved, we had to rely on data reported in the Hospital In-patient Inquiry which (then) distinguished only patients with and without medical card cover. (About two-thirds of those not covered by a medical card have private health insurance.) Analysis of acute in-patients revealed important differences in bed-day consumption and case-mix intensity. In 1996 and 1997, patients with medical card cover accounted for 44 per cent of the discharges from public hospitals but for about 54 per cent of all bed-days, and had an average length of stay about 25 per cent longer than non-medical card patients.

This was clearly related to the differing age profiles of the two groups, with the average age of medical card patients be-ing almost 50 compared with only 38 for other patients. This had major implications for both the nature of the conditions oc-curring in each group and the care provided. In particular, medical card patients were more likely to have been treated for a medical condition, and the non-medical card patients were more likely to have had a surgical procedure, when in hospital. Within Diagnosis Related Groups, medical card patients still tended to have longer average length of stay.

Private Care and Resource Use

We then explore the implications of the differences in the types of care provided for the resource use of these two groups, again with medical card status serving as a proxy for differ-ences between public and private patients. Non-medical card patients are found to be more costly per day spent in hospital. In terms of the costs taken into account in the Department of Health and Children's specialty costing exercise, the case-mix adjusted cost per day spent in hospital by a non-medical card patient in 1997 was estimated at £246, compared with £230 for GMS patients. This assumes that the same average costs within specialty can reasonably be applied to both private and public patients, and does not incorporate all costs.

While tentative, given all the gaps in the information currently available, with about one in five patients in public hospitals receiving private care, and that care more costly on a per-night basis than the care received by public patients, it appears that about one-quarter of the direct cost of providing inpatient care in public hospitals may be attributable to private patients. Concentrating on direct costs only, these initial estimates suggested that private patients may have accounted for about £130 million in expenditure on direct provision of care in 1996. This amounted to about twice the income from charges for private accommodation in that year, with private patients also subsidised through tax relief on health insurance premia.

The Demand for Health Insurance

What implications would increasing charges for private care in public hospitals have for the demand for private insurance, the major mechanism through which the demand for private care itself would be affected? Time-series analysis of data on the evolution of health insurance in Ireland was explored but the results were unsatisfactory, because potentially important explanatory variables relating to perceptions of the public health service could not be included. Household survey data allowed those with health insurance to be profiled in depth, revealing for example that while coverage rises markedly with household income, some of those covered are in the bottom half of the household income distribution and a significant minority at the top do not have cover. This highlights the extent to which health insurance cover has penetrated in recent years well beyond the upper reaches of the income distribution and social class hierarchy. An increase in the frequency of employer provision of health insurance as a benefit was also noted.

Results from an attitudinal survey carried out in 1999 also shed a good deal of light on why people buy health insurance. Almost all those who had insurance said being sure of getting into hospital was an important reason. However, being sure of getting good treatment, being sure of getting consultant care, and fear of large hospital bills were also very widely regarded as important. Compared with the pattern of responses from a similar exercise carried out in 1991, quality of care appeared to have become somewhat more important. Those with insurance appeared relatively insensitive to a price increase next year of the order of 10-20 per cent, though over one-third said they would be very likely to give up insurance if the price went up by 50 per cent.

Recent experience suggests that the forces leading to increasing demand for health insurance in the Irish case are powerful. Both attitudinal responses and this recent experience suggest that annual increases in the cost of insurance in excess of those recently seen, while they might indeed be enough to cause the rate of increase in numbers insured to tail off for a time, would not be enough in themselves to produce a dramatic reduction in the numbers insured. This is of course dependent on the forces promoting demand for insurance continuing to operate. Two key influences are likely to be economic growth, and perceptions of the care available to public patients and availability of that care, as reflected in indicators available to the public, such as waiting lists.

Access to Hospital Care

The arrangements for access to care for public versus private patients in public hospitals introduced in the early 1990s involved designating most beds in public hospitals as for public or private use, and monitoring the extent of "crossover" of private patients into public beds. About 23 per cent of all in-patient bed-days spent by private patients in public hospitals were in beds designated as public. A slightly smaller absolute number of bed-days was spent by public patients in designated private beds. A substantial proportion of this crossover was in a small number of hospitals. The key factor identified by hospital management leading to private patients being accommodated in public beds was admission through accident/emergency departments of patients opting (either then or subsequently) for private status when no private bed was available. Improvements to the reporting and monitoring of the arrangements could be piloted in those hospitals where "crossover" is most prevalent, before assessing their effectiveness. Changes in the complex structure of incentives facing consultants and hospitals could also significantly alter the nature of the regulation required to promote equity of access.

Improving the Information Base

The study also identifies areas where improved data is a priority. The absence of information on cost of private versus public patients within specialities is a major limitation. A breakdown by public/private status for the specialty costing exercise could be introduced gradually, beginning with those cost centres where the public/private breakdown is most significant. Data on waiting lists for public patients for specified procedures are gathered by the Department of Health and Children, but length of time spent between referral and first specialist consultation is also important, as is information on waiting times for private patients.

Chapter 1

Introduction

1.1 Introduction

Ireland's health services are a complex and sometimes confusing mixture of public and private provision and financing. This is particularly true in the crucial area of acute hospital services. "Private" care is received not only in private hospitals, but also in public hospitals largely financed by the state. This is because many public hospitals, as well as providing care to public patients, have private accommodation catering for the private patients of their consultant doctors. Private health insurance in Ireland has up until recently mostly been targeted at the cost of in-patient hospital care, and covering the charges for this private care in public hospitals has been one of the main roles of health insurance in Ireland.

This structure gives rise to a number of issues about efficiency and equity in delivering acute hospital services, which are the focus of the present study. Originally commissioned by the Department of Health and Children,[1] it aims first to assess the extent of private practice within the public hospital sector, the characteristics of the case-mix being dealt with, and the costs associated with provision of that care. The stated intention of public policy is to move to charging the full cost of provision for such private practice in public hospitals, so a key issue for this study is the gap between that cost and the current level of charges.

---

[1] Views expressed in the study are of course those of the authors.

We then turn to the impact of closing that gap on demand for health insurance, which involves an in-depth consideration of the factors underlying that demand and its likely sensitivity to price. Finally, we consider the adequacy of the arrangements currently in place regarding equity of access for public patients, which involve *inter alia* the designation of beds as private versus public and the monitoring of their use.

We begin by providing in the next section a description of the role which private practice in public hospitals currently plays within the Irish health care system. In doing so, we highlight some broader issues raised by the public/private mix in the hospital sector (including private hospitals) and indeed within the health care system as a whole. These broader issues are beyond the scope of this study, but are an important part of the context in which it has to be seen. The final section of this introductory chapter sets out the content and analytic approach of the various parts of the study, so that the reader has a clear picture of how these different elements fit together.

1.2 The Institutional and Policy Context

About one-quarter of all health care spending in Ireland comes from private sources, with the remaining three-quarters coming from the state. This private expenditure mostly comprises household expenditure on general practitioner visits and pharmaceuticals, and health insurance companies' spending on private hospital care.[2] Up to the mid-1990s, almost all this health insurance was provided by a state-backed non-profit insurer, the Voluntary Health Insurance (VHI) Board. The health insurance market was opened up to competition following the Health Insurance Act of 1994 and BUPA Ireland entered the market in 1996.

About half of all health expenditure goes on acute hospital services — this figure has declined over the last decade but hospital care remains the dominant item in the national health budget. Public hospitals are classified into two types, Health

---

[2] While some of the household spending is on private hospital care and some of the insurance spending is not, most of the spending is split in this way.

Board and voluntary hospitals, reflecting the historical evolution of the present structure. Health Board hospitals are owned, financed and administered directly by the state's regional health authorities under their general hospital care programmes. Public voluntary hospitals, on the other hand, are owned and operated by religious orders and lay boards of governors. They are now largely financed by state funds, either directly from the central Department of Health and Children or through the recently established Eastern Regional Health Authority covering Dublin and surrounding areas.

As well as these public hospitals, there are around 20 private hospitals, most of whom are members of the Independent Hospital Association. This private hospital sector receives no direct government funding, and is run on a non-profit basis.

Crucially for the present study, private hospital care is provided not only in these private hospitals, but also in many public hospitals. These public hospitals have private or semi-private accommodation, and patients opting for this accommodation are liable for a maintenance charge. A patient who is being treated privately by a medical consultant in a public hospital will normally have this private accommodation arranged by that consultant. This scope to treat their private patients within the public hospital system is an integral part of the contract many consultants work under, and is seen by them as of central importance.

So what does private care and being a private patient actually mean in this situation? To capture the nuances involved, one needs an understanding of the structure of entitlement to public care and how this has evolved, since that determines how a public patient is defined and treated. From the late 1950s, all but about 15 per cent of the Irish population had entitlement from the state to care as a public patient in a public hospital without charge. The top 15 per cent in terms of earnings were treated as private patients and up to 1979 had to pay both maintenance charges and the cost of consultant in-patient care. The creation of the VHI in the late 1950s, as a state-backed insurer which operated community rating and with income tax relief on premia, was designed to cater for this high-income group. In effect, those towards the top of the earnings distribution were encouraged to take out health insurance and facilitated in doing so, while the cost of in-patient care for the rest of the population was fully covered by the state. In 1979 eligibility for treatment in public hospitals without charge was extended to the entire population, but an upper income limit was retained excluding again about the top 15 per cent from free consultant services.

Complicating the picture, only a sub-set of those entitled to public hospital care have had free primary care from the state. In a system formalised in 1970, about one-third of the population have entitlement to free general practitioner services and prescribed medicines from the state, and the rest of the population have to pay privately for those services. Which of these categories a family falls into is decided through the application of a means test determining whether one is entitled to a "medical card". The same general practitioners treat both those paying privately and those whose costs are met by the state through the General Medical Services Board. In a further complication, in 1987 statutory charges for out-patient care and in-patient nights in public hospitals were introduced, which applied to everyone not covered by a medical card (whether in public or private accommodation).

So at that point the public entitlement structure comprised three distinct groups, whose situation with respect to care in public hospitals was as follows:

- Entitlement category I (with medical card cover), entitled to free public hospital care;

- Entitlement category II, liable for the per-night and out-patient statutory charges only; and

- Entitlement category III, liable for both the statutory charges and consultant fees.

On top of this entitlement structure for public care, private care could be obtained in either public and private hospitals, and the cost of this care covered by health insurance from the state-backed VHI. So public patients were those availing of their entitlement to accommodation in a public ward of a public hospital, with their medical care provided by a combination of non-consultant doctors engaged full-time on those duties or by consultant doctors whose contracts were to either work full-time or part-time in the public system. Someone opting to be the private patient of a consultant, on the other hand, would have their hospital care arranged by that consultant. This could be either in private hospitals, or where the consultant had that scope it could be in private accommodation in public hospitals, or indeed on occasion in a public ward of a public hospital if no private bed was available.

This system of entitlement and provision which had evolved by the late 1980s well merited Barrington's (1987) description of "an extraordinary symbiosis of public and private medicine" (p. 285). As she put it, private practice was accepted and facilitated in a number of ways. Means testing ensured that roughly 70 per cent of the population had to pay their general practitioner and 15 per cent their hospital specialist. Hospital consultants had the use of the staff and facilities of the public hospital service to treat their patients, at little or no cost to the doctor and at a subsidised cost to the patient — this subsidy being a central concern of the present study. Patients in private accommodation in public hospitals were charged only the marginal cost of that accommodation, apparently on the basis that they had already contributed to the overall cost of the public system through taxation. In combination with tax relief on the cost of health insurance, this effective subsidy meant that the net cost of private care to patients was held down. Insurance was then much less costly than it would otherwise have been, and by the mid-1980s the numbers insured were more than twice the 15 per cent who had to pay consultant fees.

As Barrington highlighted, one consequence was a growth in private hospital care and increasing concern that subsidies to private care were jeopardising the principle, first established in the 1930s, that all patients, whether rich or poor, should be treated in the same hospital by the same medical and nursing staff. A related concern, which is more directly relevant to the present study, relates to access to and care in public hospitals.

This concern was reflected for example in the deliberations of the Commission on Health Funding, appointed by the Minister for Health in 1987. This Commission noted in its Report that

> "There is a major problem regarding access to public hos-
> pitals; the common perception is that those opting for pri-
> vate care are able to obtain admission more quickly than
> those using the public system" (1989, p. 19).

They also noted public perception that private care — whether in public or private hospital — was higher-quality care with a greater degree of personal attention from the consultant rather than the more junior medical staff. The Report went on to say that the Commission's discussions with those involved left them in no doubt that these perceptions were accurate. In some cases speedy access to necessary treatment was determined by ability to pay rather than medical need, and that this dispar-ity was most marked where it concerned access to the same public hospital rather than to private hospitals (p. 234). This, the Commission felt, would partly explain the substantial take-up of health insurance.

The Commission regarded this situation as failing to meet the definition of equity they adopted, which was ensuring equal access to and utilisation of necessary services for patients with similar needs, irrespective of differences in their ability to pay. To eliminate this inequity, the Commission recommended the introduction of a common waiting list for all admissions to pub-lic hospitals — whether to public or private accommodation — from which cases would be taken in order of medically estab-lished priority. The Commission argued that the existence of private or semi-private beds in public hospitals should not de-termine the choice of patients to be admitted. If at a particular point public ward accommodation was fully taken up, a hospital should admit the patient with priority on the basis of medical need to whatever level of accommodation was available. The Commission envisaged that the overall balance between public and private admissions would then be monitored.

This approach — which faced both practical and conceptual problems — was not adopted. Instead, the Programme for Economic and Social Progress ushered in several related changes designed to promote equity. First, as recommended by the Commission, the system of health services eligibility was altered by abolishing what was then Entitlement Category III, which gave limited entitlement to the top 15 per cent of the population in terms of coverage for hospital care. This meant that the public entitlement structure now in operation has two categories. Those with medical card cover are entitled to free public hospital care, whereas those without that cover have to pay the statutory charges for in-patient night and out-patient visits.

Secondly, the Programme for Economic and Social Progress agreed between the social partners promised to introduce new arrangements for admission to public wards in public hospitals. The stated aim was to arrive at a situation whereby private patients availing of public hospitals for elective (non-emergency) treatment would eventually be accommodated only in private or semi-private beds. New arrangements were introduced whereby, following discussions with hospital and Health Board management as well as the medical organisations, most acute beds in public hospitals were designated by the Department of Health (as it then was) as either public or private beds. Legislative underpinnings were provided by the 1991 Health (Amendment) Act. On a phased basis over a period of three years, hospitals were to introduce systems to restrict access of private patients to public beds. Reporting mechanisms were also introduced so that the use of public beds by private patients could be monitored.

These arrangements aimed at directly addressing a specific aspect of access to care in public hospitals, both by setting up mechanisms to restrict private patients to private beds, and by increasing policy-makers' control over the mix of public and private beds. While such policy concerns represent one of the main topics of the present study, they are embedded in broader issues about the public-private mix in public hospitals, and in particular about the appropriate financial relationship between public and private care. When patients in private accommodation in public hospitals were paying for their own consultant care, they were in effect charged only the marginal cost of that accommodation. The cost to the patient was thus unrelated to the resources used in providing that care, involving as it did the non-consultant staff and facilities of the hospital. From the point when Entitlement Category III was abolished, the per-night charge for private and semi-private accommodation in public hospitals has been increased significantly, the explicit aim being to reduce the extent of subsidisation of private patients. The current level of this charge is still widely regarded as well below the cost of the resources employed in treating these patients, and the stated intention of public policy is now to move towards charging the full cost of providing private hospital care.

The extent of this implicit subsidy and the scale of increase in charges to private patients required to eliminate it is a central focus of this present study. In addition, though, the downstream impact of increasing charges for private care in public hospitals is one of our main themes, in particular the impact on the demand for private care and, by extension, for private health insurance. Apart from the evolving institutional setting, the most dramatic feature of the public-private mix in the Irish healthcare system has been the continuing growth in the numbers with private health insurance. By the close of the 1990s this exceeded 40 per cent of the population. The fact that a system effectively designed for a situation where 15-20 per cent of the population had private insurance now has more than twice that number with cover for private care through insurance poses fundamental questions for public policy.

From the mid-1990s, the nature of the health insurance market itself has changed in response to European Union regulations, and brings with it a further set of challenges for policymakers. New legislation has opened up the market to competing insurers, though these are obliged to operate community rating, and a risk equalisation fund is to redistribute profits in order to offset the impact of any "cherry-picking" of younger healthier subscribers. So far, only the British insurer BUPA has entered the market and now insures around 4 per cent of the population, with the VHI remaining dominant in terms of market share. Income tax relief on health insurance premia is also now available only at the standard tax rate rather than the top tax rate one is paying.

The factors driving the increase in numbers with health insurance are examined in depth in the course of this study. It represents a key aspect of the rapidly changing context in which various aspects of the public/private mix in the Irish healthcare system are now being debated, in particular from an equity perspective. Particular elements of the public policy response have now been clearly articulated — such as the importance of preserving community rating in health insurance and moving towards charging the full cost of private care in public hospitals. However, the overall strategy on the public/private mix within which these elements are set is less clear. It is therefore worth concluding this contextual discussion with a focus on the main levers available to policy-makers under the current structure allowing them to affect the demand for and supply of private care in public hospitals. Altering the level and structure of charges for private care in public hospitals will clearly influence demand, although this is mediated through insurers who have scope to affect precisely how those increasing costs are passed on to the consumer. Further reducing tax reliefs on premia would increase the cost of health insurance, and other things being equal reduce the demand for insurance and by extension for private care.

Other policy levers available within the present structure affect supply of rather than the demand for private care. The number of private beds in public hospitals and the — intimately related — contractual relationship between the public system and hospital consultant doctors represent the two most important supply-side levers. Their importance can be illustrated by experience. When the public finances were being brought under control in the late 1980s, public hospital bed numbers were cut back while private beds in those hospitals were increased. This both maximised public revenue from private patients, and accorded with the desire of many consultants to have private beds available to treat the growing numbers with insurance. The number of private beds in public hospitals has been held stable in more recent years, implying a resistance to further growth in private care in public hospitals.

The economic incentives currently facing the different agents involved in private care in public hospitals, and how these might best be reoriented, merit careful consideration. Hospital consultants currently receive payment (from the VHI) for treating patients in public hospitals who opt for private status, whether they are accommodated in public or private beds. The hospital, on the other hand, receives payment only where a private bed is occupied. Increasing levels of income over the anticipated level from delivering private care in private beds add to the resources available to the hospital in a given year, though over time there appears to be some clawback as public funding adjusts to the expected level of private revenue. The fully insured patient is financially unaffected by whether private care is received in a public or private hospital, and in the former by whether a public or private bed is occupied. The insurer pays most for care of its customers when that care is received in a private hospital, less than that when it is delivered in a private bed in a public hospital, and least when it is delivered in a public bed. Changes in this complex structure of incentives could significantly alter the nature of the regulation required to promote equity of access.

Of course, the current institutional structure is not cast in stone, but that raises issues much broader than those tackled in this study. Here our focus is on more limited but nonetheless critical and indeed complex questions. What is the current extent and nature of private care in public hospitals? What is in fact the relationship between the current level of charges for private care in public hospitals and the cost of providing this care? If charging the full cost for that care substantially increased charges, what impact would that be likely to have on demand? Since this demand effectively operates through insurance, what are the factors fuelling the growth in numbers insured, and how sensitive is that likely to be to increasing cost? Are the current arrangements for ensuring that private patients in public hospitals are treated in private accommodation operating effectively?

Limitations in the available data make it difficult to answer some of these questions with confidence. This study seeks to set out clearly both what can be learned from available information and where that information base needs to be improved. In the rest of this chapter we outline the structure within which our analysis and findings are presented, together with the main sources of data employed.

1.3 Outline of the Study

The study contains a number of different but related elements. We begin in Chapter 2 by looking at the current stock of public and private beds in acute public hospitals and how this has been evolving, drawing on administrative data. These stock figures are not enough on their own to capture the public/private mix in bed use, since public patients are on occasion treated in private beds and vice versa: one needs information on the public/private status of patients as well as beds. Public hospitals report to the Department of Health and Children on a regular basis on the usage of beds by public versus private patients, in the course of monitoring the usage of beds designated as for public or private use. This provides a measure of overall public versus private use of beds in public hospitals, which we also document in Chapter 2.

In Chapter 3 we then turn from numbers of patients and beds to the private care provided within public hospitals. No information is reported via the bed monitoring system on the diagnosis of, or nature of care provided to, public versus private patients. We therefore have to rely at this point on the Hospital In-Patient Enquiry (HIPE) to measure utilisation and its case-mix. Unfortunately, HIPE did not until very recently distinguish public and private patients, but we were able to look at differences between those with and without medical card cover. This in effect provides a baseline for the private/public patient split. Chapter 3 also looks at how the data available on patterns of care might be improved, informed *inter alia* by discussions with the larger public hospitals about the nature of their administrative recording systems.

We then focus in Chapter 4 on the cost of providing this private care within public hospitals. The Department of Health and Children produces, and provided to us, data on average cost of provision (across public and private patients) by specialty, used in its hospital budgeting. This, taken together with the case-mix for medical card versus non-medical card patients shown by HIPE and presented in Chapter 3, can be used to produce what are in effect proxies, first estimates of the cost of provision of care to private patients in public hospitals. In addition, the larger public hospitals were once again canvassed to explore the extent to which they have data bearing on the resources used by public versus private patients. This information provides a basis on which to assess how much the current level of charges would have to be raised in order to cover the resources used.

Our main objective is then to assess the likely effect that moving towards charging the cost of provision would have on demand for private care, and by extension for health insurance. This relies first on our estimates, necessarily highly tentative, of that cost. To inform this analysis of responsiveness we undertook three distinct but related analytical exercises, described in Chapters 5 and 6. First, we analyse the way in which the demand for health insurance has evolved over time in Ireland, and seek to relate this to factors one might expect to be important influences. We then present results from an in-depth analysis of the characteristics of those who have and do not have health insurance at a point in time. We use for this purpose data from the *Living in Ireland* household survey carried out by the ESRI in 1994, supplemented by more recent data from a follow-up survey in 1997. Thirdly, in Chapter 6 we present results from a specially designed survey aimed at exploring attitudinal aspects of health insurance demand, carried out by the ESRI as part of the present study.

We then turn to the adequacy of the arrangements currently in place regarding access for public versus private patients to public hospital care. Chapter 7 first presents a description of these arrangements, which involve designating beds as for public or private patients and monitoring their use. In order to assess how effective this is in ensuring equity in access, as set out in the Department of Health and Children's Health Strategy, we first look at the public/private usage of designated public versus private beds as reported by hospitals to the Department. Data on waiting lists gathered by the Department, which cover the length of time public patients wait for certain procedures from time of diagnosis, are also discussed.

We summarise the results of these different elements in Chapter 8. We then draw on those findings to assess the likely impact of moving towards charging private patients in public hospitals the cost of provision of care, and the implications for policy aimed at meeting the principles of the health strategy in relation to equity, quality and accountability.

Chapter 2

Public versus Private Beds and Patients in Public Hospitals

2.1 Introduction

In this chapter we begin our analysis of the public/private mix in public hospitals in Ireland by looking at the mix of beds and of patients in terms of this public/private distinction. Section 2.2 examines the stock of public versus private beds and how this evolved over the 1990s, the period for which most suitable data is available. Section 2.3 looks at the numbers of public versus private patients treated in public hospitals and how this developed over the same period. In concluding, Section 2.4 points to the analysis of the types of care received, which is developed in the next chapter.

2.2 Public and Private Beds in Public Hospitals

The distinction between public and private beds in Irish public hospitals has not always been easy to draw. Up to the early 1990s a particular bed could sometimes in effect change status from day to day depending on the public/private status of the patient occupying it. In 1991, the public healthcare entitlement system was altered with the abolition of Category III, placing all those without medical card cover on an equal footing in terms of public entitlements, as described in detail in Chapter 1. At the same time, new arrangements were introduced whereby, following discussions with hospital and Health Board management as well as the medical organisations, most acute beds in public hospitals were designated by the Department of Health (as it then was) as either public or private beds. Legislative underpinnings were provided by the 1991 Health (Amendment) Act. As a result, one can now talk in terms of the stock of public versus private beds with much greater precision.

The number of overnight beds designated as public and as private in acute public hospitals in 1991, 1993 and 1999 is shown in Table 2.1.[1] A small proportion of beds are not designated as either public or private, for example those in intensive care units. We see that the number not designated in this manner was higher at the outset but by 1993 had fallen to about 6 per cent of all overnight beds, similar to the proportion in 1999. The proportion of all overnight beds designated as private (including semi-private) was 19 per cent at the outset in 1991. It was 20 per cent in 1993, after the introductory period, and remains at that level in 1999. There is only a marginal difference in this respect between Health Board and voluntary hospitals, with the latter having a slightly higher proportion of beds designated as private (20.8 per cent compared with 19.5 per cent).

TABLE 2.1: DESIGNATED PUBLIC AND PRIVATE OVERNIGHT BEDS IN ACUTE PUBLIC HOSPITALS, 1991, 1993 AND 1999

	Public	Private/Semi-private	Non-designated	Total
1991				
Health Board hospitals	4,846	1,159	500	6,505
Voluntary Hospitals	3,710	1,066	375	5,151
All acute hospitals	8,556	2,225	875	11,656
1993				
Health Board hospitals	4,985	1,218	342	6,545
Voluntary Hospitals	3,688	1,112	383	5,183
All acute hospitals	8,673	2,330	725	11,728
1999				
Health Board hospitals	5,254	1,362	372	6,988
Voluntary Hospitals	3,366	985	391	4,742
All acute hospitals	8,620	2,347	763	11,730

[1] These figures relate to June 1991, August 1993 and February 1999.

Day beds are also included in the bed designation arrangements, and Table 2.2 shows the distribution of these beds between public and private in each of the years. We see that the
total number of day beds in acute public hospitals has increased from 457 in 1991 to 562 in 1999. The number not designated as public or private has fallen from 37 in 1991 to only 6 in
1999. The proportion designated as private was 27 per cent in
1991, at the initiation of the system, and had risen to 32 per cent
by 1999. In this case a slightly higher proportion of day beds in
Health Board than voluntary hospitals are designated private.

**TABLE 2.2: DESIGNATED PUBLIC AND PRIVATE DAY BEDS IN
ACUTE PUBLIC HOSPITALS, 1991, 1993 AND 1999**

	Public	Private/Semi-private	Non-designated	Total
1991				
Health Board hospitals	121	56	23	200
Voluntary Hospitals	175	68	14	257
All acute hospitals	296	124	37	457
1993				
Health Board hospitals	140	72	0	212
Voluntary Hospitals	203	98	14	315
All acute hospitals	343	170	14	527
1999				
Health Board hospitals	167	86	0	253
Voluntary Hospitals	208	95	6	309
All acute hospitals	375	181	6	562

2.3 Public and Private Patients in Public Hospitals

We now turn from beds to patients. Once again, it has not always been possible to distinguish the numbers of patients
treated in public hospitals as private versus public ones, but
reporting mechanisms for hospitals introduced in association
with the bed designation exercise by the Department of Health
from the early 1990s have considerably improved this situation.
The admission arrangements these mechanisms are intended to

monitor are discussed in more detail in Chapter 6, when we hone in on the relationship between the public/private status of the patients and the type of bed they occupy. Here, however, we use data reported by hospitals to the Department to simply capture the overall numbers of private versus public patients treated in public hospitals.

It is important to be clear about how private versus public patients are distinguished for this purpose. The definition of private status is not simply whether the individual has private health insurance coverage. Rather, the definition is that the patient is opting to avail of private consultant services, rather than public consultant services available to everyone. Someone could have health insurance but opt to be treated as a public patient, while not everyone opting to avail of private consultant services need have insurance. Patients admitted through accident/emergency departments may opt at the time of admission or subsequently to have private status.

Data for 1995-1997 have been provided to us by the Department of Health and Children, and Table 2.3 shows the number of bed-days (excluding day beds) in public hospitals used by public and private patients overall in each of these years. This reveals an upward trend in the proportion of bed-days accounted for by private patients, from 18 per cent in 1995 to 19 per cent in 1996 and 20 per cent in 1997.

TABLE 2.3: PUBLIC VERSUS PRIVATE USAGE IN PUBLIC HOSPITALS (EXCLUDING DAY BEDS), 1995-1997

	Total bed days used by public patients	Total bed days used by private patients	Total bed days used by all patients	Private percentage of total
1995	2,700,961	604,668	3,305,629	18.3
1996	2,699,021	634,916	3,333,937	19.0
1997	2,700,262	683,340	3,383,601	20.2

A similar analysis can be carried out for day beds used, again on the basis of the figures reported to the Department via the monitoring system. Table 2.4 shows the public/private usage pattern for day beds in 1995, 1996 and 1997. We see that about

19 per cent of day bed use in these years was by private patients, very similar to the proportion of in-patient days.

TABLE 2.4: PUBLIC VERSUS PRIVATE DAY BED USAGE IN PUBLIC HOSPITALS, 1995-1997

Hospital	Total used by public patients	Total used by private patients	Total used by all patients	Percentage used by private patients
1995	108,735	26,320	135,055	19.5
1996	127,992	30,198	158,190	19.1
1997	137,380	30,715	168,095	18.3

2.4 Conclusion

In this chapter we began our analysis of private practice in public hospitals by focusing first on the stock of public versus private beds. The new arrangements for access to care for public versus private patients in public hospitals introduced in the early 1990s involved designating most beds in acute public hospitals as for either public or private use. Under the arrangements, private patients are defined as those opting to avail of private consultant services, rather than simply someone who has private health insurance cover. About 20 per cent of in-patient beds in acute public hospitals are currently designated as being for private patient use, while about 32 per cent of day beds are so designated. Turning to patients rather than beds, we saw that the proportion of all bed-days spent in public hospitals accounted for by private patients rose from 18 per cent in 1995 to 21 per cent in 1997, with private patients accounting for about the same proportion of day bed use.

Chapter 3

Public versus Private Utilisation in Public Hospitals

3.1 Introduction

To establish the balance between public and private workload in public hospitals, it is not enough to simply compare the numbers of public versus private patients treated: one also has to look at the nature of the care provided to each group. Unfortunately, no comprehensive data on the public versus private care provided in public hospitals was available when we were carrying out this study. The regular Hospital In-Patient Inquiry (HIPE), whereby public hospitals record and report on their activity levels, contains detailed information reported by hospitals on the length of stay and nature of care provided to each patient, and is in that respect an extremely rich source. However, the information provided by hospitals through HIPE available for analysis in this study did not distinguish public from private patients. Since then a classifier has been introduced in the data reported by hospitals through HIPE, and this represents a significant improvement in the data available in the future.

What the HIPE does currently allow is for those with and without medical card cover (GMS versus non-GMS) to be distinguished. Private patients can effectively be seen as a sub-set of those not covered by a medical card; just under two-thirds of adults do not have medical card cover, and just under two-thirds of those have private health insurance. (While some private patients do have medical card cover and some of those with medical cards have private health insurance, as we shall see later the 1994 *Living in Ireland Survey* suggests that the numbers involved are sufficiently small to allow this generalisation to be made). Thus the differences in the extent and nature of utilisation of public hospital care between those with and without medical card cover — which are very interesting in their own right — will also provide an indication of the differences in which we are actually most interested here, between public and private patients. We look in this chapter at the length of stay, principal procedures and case-mix of GMS versus non-GMS patients, before turning in the next chapter to the implications for resource use.

3.2 HIPE Data for 1996 and 1997

Here we analyse the HIPE data for 1996 and 1997. For all participating hospitals, the HIPE achieved 98 per cent coverage in 1996 and 97 per cent coverage in 1997.[1] For both 1996 and 1997, information on GMS status is available for over 96 per cent of total HIPE discharges. In 1996, 43.7 per cent of HIPE discharges were recorded as GMS patients compared with 44.3 per cent in 1997. Non-GMS patients accounted for 52.3 per cent of HIPE discharges in 1996 and 51.7 per cent of discharges in 1997. Despite accounting for the smaller proportion of discharges, GMS patients accounted for a higher proportion of bed-days relative to the non-GMS group over this period. In 1996, GMS patients used 53.2 per cent of total bed-days compared with 44 per cent for non-GMS patients. There were marginal changes in this estimate in 1997 with GMS and non-GMS patients accounting for 54.5 per cent and 43.7 per cent, respectively, of total bed-days. While GMS status was unknown for 4 per cent of discharges in both years, the proportion of bed-days accounted for by this group declined from 2.8 per cent in 1996 to 1.8 per cent in 1997.

---

[1] One factor which may account for the slight discrepancy is the fact that the HIPE expanded in 1997 to include obstetrics so there has been a change in the way both the numerator and denominator are estimated between the two years.

In 1996, 1.9 per cent of discharges had an average length of stay in excess of 30 days and the comparable estimate for 1997 was 1.7 per cent. Because discharges with exceptionally long lengths of stay can distort prevailing trends for particular patient groups, it was decided for this stage of the analysis of GMS status of HIPE discharges to limit consideration to inpatients with an average length of stay of 0-30 days. For this group of discharges, the average length of stay (LOS) for GMS patients was 5.98 days in 1996 compared with 4.8 days for non-GMS patients. In 1997 there were very small changes in these indicators as GMS patients had a LOS of 5.96 days and the LOS for non-GMS patients was 4.67 days. So the average length of stay was 25 per cent longer for GMS patients than non-GMS patients in 1996, increasing to 28 per cent in 1997.

To understand why this comes about and its implications we need first to take the differing age profiles of the two groups into account. We now present and comment on tables containing analyses of GMS and non-GMS discharges for 1996 and 1997, looking first in Table 3.1 at the age distribution. While there is limited change from one year to the next in the age distribution within the GMS and non-GMS groups, Table 3.1 shows that there are marked differences in the age profile between these two groups. Overall, GMS discharges are generally older and in 1996 and 1997 the average age among this group is close to 50 years compared with the average age of 38 years estimated for non-GMS discharges in both years. Apart from the 0-4 category which accounts for a high proportion of discharges in all groups, the highest concentration of GMS discharges is found in the categories over 65 years, while the non-GMS discharges are heavily concentrated in the 20-40 age groups.

TABLE 3.1: AGE DISTRIBUTION (%) FOR GMS AND NON-GMS PATIENTS: 1996, 1997

Age	1996		1997	
	GMS	*Non-GMS*	*GMS*	*Non-GMS*
0 to 4	8.18	11.60	7.69	11.21
5 to 9	4.06	5.14	3.59	4.46
10 to 14	4.19	5.07	3.79	4.59
15 to 19	4.69	6.76	4.97	6.69
20 to 24	4.00	7.26	4.40	7.51
25 to 29	3.22	7.27	3.62	8.42
30 to 34	3.39	7.50	3.54	9.00
35 to 39	3.57	6.30	3.65	6.89
40 to 44	3.72	5.38	3.77	5.37
45 to 49	4.08	5.45	4.24	5.14
50 to 54	4.27	5.32	4.33	5.21
55 to 59	4.39	5.03	4.45	4.81
60 to 64	5.72	5.10	5.90	4.94
65 to 69	8.10	4.97	8.00	4.70
70 to 74	10.54	4.53	10.24	4.27
75 to 79	10.26	3.60	10.21	3.38
80 to 84	8.41	2.29	8.13	2.10
85 to 89	3.90	1.04	4.13	0.96
90 +	1.31	0.39	1.34	0.35
Total	100.00	100.00	100.00	100.00
Average age (years)	49.50	37.74	49.84	37.71
No. of Discharges	209,636	227,700	215,664	236,084

For the age standardised analyses presented in this section the age groups are collapsed into three broad categories as follows: children aged 0-14, adults aged 15-64 and the elderly aged 65+. The number of discharges, together with the Per Centage distribution, for the GMS and non-GMS groups in 1996 and 1997 are presented in Table 3.1a. The concentration of non-GMS discharges in the so called adult group is clearly in evidence here with over 60 per cent in each year. For the GMS group, there is a similar number of discharges in the adult and elderly categories in each year.

TABLE 3.1A: SUMMARY DISTRIBUTION OF GMS AND NON-GMS DISCHARGES BY AGE CATEGORY

		1996		1997	
		Discharges	*Per Cent*	*Discharges*	*Per Cent*
GMS	Children	34,453	16.4%	32,493	15.1%
	Adults	86,045	41.0%	92,475	42.9%
	Elderly	89,138	42.5%	90,696	42.1%
	Total	**209,636**	**100.0%**	**215,664**	**100.0%**
Non-GMS	Children	49,674	21.8%	47,834	20.3%
	Adults	139,736	61.4%	151,045	64.0%
	Elderly	38,290	16.8%	37,205	15.8%
	Total	**227,700**	**100.0%**	**236,084**	**100.0%**

Inpatients with LOS 0-30 days

3.3. Principal Diagnosis by GMS Status

The age differential between GMS and non-GMS discharges noted in the previous section has implications for the nature of the conditions occurring in each group. Tables 3.2a and 3.2b present the high ranking principal diagnoses for GMS and non-GMS discharges for 1996 while the comparable information for 1997 is presented in Tables 3.2c and 3.2d. In addition to presenting the proportion of discharges accounted for by each diagnosis, the average length of stay, the bed-days used and the associated morbidity code (ICD-9-CM[2]) are also included. For the GMS group, there is a higher level of concentration in the top 30 diagnoses which account for close to 27 per cent of discharges in both 1996 and 1997. By comparison, just 23 per cent of non-GMS discharges are estimated among the 30 highest ranked diagnoses for both years. Respiratory conditions, which

---

[2] *The International Classification of Diseases, 9th edition, clinical modification* (ICD-9-CM) is used for coding diagnoses and procedures within the Irish Hospital Inpatient Enquiry.

are strongly associated with the older age groups, are very
much in evidence for both groups of discharges while the more
youthful age profile, together with the expansion of the HIPE to
include obstetrical cases, probably accounts, to some extent,
for the increased number of obstetrical/gynaecological conditions in evidence for the non-GMS group in 1997.

**TABLE 3.2A: TOP 30 PRINCIPAL DIAGNOSES FOR GMS PATIENTS,
1996**

ICD-9-CM	Principal Diagnosis	Per Cent	LOS	Bed Days
49121	Obstructive chronic bronchitis with acute exacerbation	2.18	8.32	37,940
5198	Respiratory system disease NEC	1.65	7.04	24,398
36610	Senile cataract NOS	1.25	3.18	8,321
481	Pneumococcal pneumonia	1.24	8.37	21,706
5990	Urinary tract infection NOS	1.16	6.09	14,792
4280	Congestive heart failure	1.13	9.49	22,560
4111	Intermediate coronary syndrome	1.11	7.19	16,686
78650	Chest pain NOS	1.10	4.04	9,341
49390	Asthma w/o status asthmaticus	1.04	3.89	8,457
5589	Noninfectious gastroenteritis NEC	1.03	4.27	9,256
V581	Chemotherapy encounter	0.93	2.72	5,295
85401	Brain injury NEC-no coma	0.89	2.04	3,785
4659	Acute upper respiratory infections NOS	0.84	3.97	6,998
42731	Atrial fibrillation	0.80	6.90	11,556
71595	Osteoarthrosis NOS-pelvis	0.79	12.49	20,643
41401	Cornary atherosclerosis of native coronary artery	0.77	8.17	13,123
600	Hyperplasia of prostate	0.72	7.38	11,199
7802	Syncope and collapse	0.70	5.10	7,480
36617	Mature cataract	0.69	3.86	5,540
5640	Constipation	0.67	4.54	6,385
4740	Chronic tonsillitis	0.66	2.75	3,789
5409	Acute appendicitis NOS	0.66	4.66	6,405
486	Pneumonia, organism NOS	0.65	8.36	11,349

ICD-9-CM	Principal Diagnosis	Per Cent	LOS	Bed Days
496	Chronic airway obstruction NEC	0.64	8.40	11,300
78903	Right lower quadrant abdominal pain	0.63	3.23	4,249
55090	Unilateral inguinal hernia	0.62	4.07	5,274
463	Acute tonsillitis	0.61	2.64	3,388
4281	Left heart failure	0.61	8.07	10,283
56210	Diverticulosis of colon	0.58	6.59	8,038
4549	Varicose vein of leg NOS	0.57	2.65	3,185
All		26.91	5.90	332,721

TABLE 3.2B: TOP 30 PRINCIPAL DIAGNOSIS FOR NON-GMS PATIENTS, 1996

ICD-9-CM	Principal Diagnosis	Per Cent	LOS	Bed Days
85401	Brain injury NEC-no coma	1.27	1.70	4,907
5409	Acute appendicitis NOS	1.26	4.30	12,330
4740	Chronic tonsillitis	1.03	2.86	6,730
49390	Asthma w/o status asthmaticus	1.02	3.19	7,404
5589	Noninfectious gastroenteritis NEC	1.01	3.18	7,330
63491	Spontaneous abortion w/o un-complication-incomplete	0.99	1.70	3,839
78650	Chest pain NOS	0.99	3.43	7,761
4659	Acute upper respiratory infections NOS	0.85	2.84	5,478
463	Acute tonsillitis	0.84	2.69	5,139
4549	Varicose vein of leg NOS	0.83	2.37	4,466
5990	Urinary tract infection NOS	0.82	4.86	9,107
55090	Unilateral inguinal hernia	0.79	3.30	5,961
07999	Viral infection NOS	0.79	2.35	4,233
5198	Respiratory system disease NEC	0.78	5.37	9,589
V581	Chemotherapy encounter	0.76	2.73	4,719
41401	Coronary atherosclerosis of native coronary artery	0.75	7.21	12,289
481	Pneumococcal pneumonia	0.74	7.44	12,560
85402	Brain injury NEC with brief loss of consciousness	0.73	1.90	3,146
6262	Excessive menstruation	0.70	4.09	6,546

ICD-9-CM	Principal Diagnosis	Per Cent	LOS	Bed Days
78903	Right lower quadrant abdominal pain	0.67	2.73	4,164
7840	Headache	0.60	3.57	4,835
42731	Atrial fibrillation	0.58	6.17	8,200
7802	Syncope and collapse	0.57	3.99	5,129
4111	Intermediate coronary syndrome	0.55	7.02	8,813
49121	Obstructive chronic bronchitis with acute exacerbation	0.53	8.49	10,290
650	Normal delivery	0.53	3.82	4,634
600	Hyperplasia of prostate	0.51	7.05	8,147
7803	Convulsions	0.51	3.10	3,560
486	Pneumonia, organism NOS	0.48	6.54	7,217
71595	Osteoarthrosis NOS-pelvis	0.48	12.57	13,712
All		22.97	4.06	212,235

TABLE 3.2C: TOP 30 PRINCIPAL DIAGNOSIS FOR GMS PATIENTS, 1997

ICD-9-CM	Principal Diagnosis	Per Cent	LOS	Bed Days
49121	Obstructive chronic bronchitis with acute exacerbation	2.79	8.30	50,018
5198	Respiratory system disease NEC	1.63	6.51	22,866
4111	Intermediate coronary syndrome	1.29	6.88	19,163
481	Pneumococcal pneumonia	1.20	8.71	22,515
5990	Urinary tract infection NOS	1.14	6.29	15,462
4280	Congestive heart failure	1.10	9.54	22,618
78650	Chest pain NOS	1.10	4.15	9,807
5589	Noninfectious gastroenteritis NEC	1.05	4.17	9,412
36610	Senile cataract NOS	1.02	3.01	6,645
41401	Coronary atherosclerosis of native coronary artery	0.95	8.06	16,545
42731	Atrial fibrillation	0.91	6.97	13,607
85401	Brain injury NEC-no coma	0.84	2.11	3,836
49390	Asthma w/o status asthmaticus	0.78	4.04	6,824
4659	Acute upper repiratory infections NOS	0.76	3.86	6,296
71595	Osteoarthrosis NOS-pelvis	0.72	12.54	19,554

ICD-9-CM	Principal Diagnosis	Per Cent	LOS	Bed Days
V581	Chemotherapy encounter	0.72	3.03	4,705
7802	Syncope and collapse	0.70	4.70	7,072
36617	Mature cataract	0.67	3.66	5,308
486	Pneumonia, organism NOS	0.66	8.02	11,430
5409	Acute appendicitis NOS	0.65	4.36	6,086
4740	Chronic tonsillitis	0.64	2.78	3,802
600	Hyperplasia of prostate	0.62	7.04	9,474
5640	Constipation	0.62	4.36	5,845
55090	Unilateral inguinal hernia	0.61	3.96	5,203
4281	Left heart failure	0.61	8.27	10,826
4661	Acute bronchiolitis	0.59	4.49	5,718
463	Acute tonsillitis	0.58	2.71	3,391
4359	Transient cerebral ischemia NOS	0.58	6.48	8,060
78903	Right lower quadrant abdominal pain	0.57	3.23	3,988
56210	Diverticulosis of colon	0.55	6.60	7,809
All		26.65	5.99	343,885

TABLE 3.2D: TOP 30 PRINCIPAL DIAGNOSIS FOR NON-GMS PATIENTS, 1997

ICD-9-CM	Principal Diagnosis	Per Cent	LOS	Bed Days
650	Normal delivery	1.371	3.770	12205
5409	Acute appendicitis NOS	1.266	4.207	12574
85401	Brain injury NEC-no coma	1.210	1.794	5126
66401	Delivery with first-degree lacerations	1.048	3.551	8784
78650	Chest pain NOS	1.028	3.498	8494
4740	Chronic tonsillitis	0.998	2.873	6767
5589	Noninfectious gastroenteritis NEC	0.955	3.308	7456
63491	Spontaneous abortion w/o complication-incomplete	0.908	1.663	3566
463	Acute tonsillitis	0.855	2.807	5664
5990	Urinary tract infection NOS	0.829	4.688	9174
41401	Coronary atherosclerosis of native coronary artery	0.795	7.287	13671

ICD-9-CM	Principal Diagnosis	Per Cent	LOS	Bed Days
49390	Asthma w/o status asthmaticus	0.776	3.180	5822
481	Pneumococcal pneumonia	0.761	7.055	12671
55090	Unilateral inguinal hernia	0.757	3.144	5615
4659	Acute upper respiratory infections NOS	0.739	2.805	4892
5198	Respiratory system disease NEC	0.730	5.193	8953
4549	Varicose vein of leg NOS	0.720	2.268	3854
65631	Fetal distress-delivered	0.705	5.466	9096
85402	Brain injury NEC with brief loss of consciousness	0.691	2.051	3348
07999	Viral infection NOS	0.687	2.415	3915
4111	Intermediate coronary syndrome	0.657	6.505	10082
78903	Right lower quadrant abdominal pain	0.654	2.837	4381
V581	Chemotherapy encounter	0.644	2.638	4013
42731	Atrial fibrillation	0.629	5.735	8522
6262	Excessive menstruation	0.613	3.999	5786
4661	Acute bronchiolitis	0.601	3.576	5075
49121	Obstructive chronic bronchitis with acute exacerbation	0.591	8.373	11689
7802	Syncope and collapse	0.532	3.828	4812
64683	Pregnancy complication NEC-antepartum	0.529	2.393	2991
78907	Generalized abdominal pain	0.528	2.666	3322
All		23.807	3.778	212320

3.4 Principal Procedures by GMS Status

The high ranking procedures reported for GMS and non-GMS discharges are reported in Tables 3.3a and 3.3b for 1996 and Tables 3.3c and 3.3d for 1997. (These tables are based on the principal surgical procedure performed and exclude cases which just had a miscellaneous diagnostic procedure.) While there is some relationship between procedures performed and the diagnostic information presented in the previous set of tables, the overlap is limited. This is due to the fact that, while a diagnosis like acute appendicitis would be expected to have an associated surgical procedure, i.e. appendectomy, many medical diagnoses, e.g. asthma or pneumonia, would not be expected to have a surgical consequence. In addition to listing the top 30 high ranking procedures and the associated ICD-9-CM codes, Tables 3.3a-3.3d present estimates for the distribution of discharges by procedure, the associated average length of stay and bed-days used.

It is interesting that while the previous set of tables showed greater concentration of GMS discharges among the group of high-ranking diagnoses, a contrasting picture is in evidence for the analysis of surgical procedures presented here. Firstly, it is worth noting that non-GMS discharges are more likely to have a surgical procedure. Over half the non-GMS discharges received a procedure (54 per cent in 1996 and 56 per cent in 1997) compared with an estimate of 43 per cent of GMS discharges in 1996 and 45 per cent in 1997. In both years, the top 30 surgical procedures accounted for around one-fifth of GMS discharges compared with one-quarter of non-GMS discharges. It is also worth noting that, for diagnoses and procedures common to both groups, in general non-GMS patients tend to have similar or shorter lengths of stay relative to the GMS patients. For example, for the diagnosis of urinary tract infection the LOS for GMS patients exceeded 6 days in both years, while the LOS for this condition for non-GMS patients was 4.9 days in 1996 and 4.7 days in 1997. The LOS for appendectomy is approximately 0.3 of a day longer for GMS patients than non-GMS patients in both years. However the older average age of GMS patients, together with the associated greater potential for more co-morbidity among this group, has to be taken into consideration in interpreting these findings.

TABLE 3.3A: TOP 30 PRINCIPAL PROCEDURES FOR GMS PATIENTS, 1996

ICD-9-CM	Principal Procedure	Per Cent	LOS	Bed days
	No procedure	57.28	5.49	559,688
5732	Cystoscopy NEC	1.27	4.74	10,677
132	Linear extracapsular lens extraction	1.13	3.72	7,478
470	Appendectomy	1.11	4.91	9,708

ICD-9-CM	Principal Procedure	Per Cent	LOS	Bed days
4516	Esophagogastroduodenoscopy with closed biopsy	1.04	8.25	15,256
6909	D & C NEC	0.98	2.40	4,195
4413	Gastroscopy NEC	0.92	7.44	12,215
1341	Phacoemulsification/aspiration of cataract	0.91	3.15	5,082
4513	Small bowel endoscopy NEC	0.81	7.19	10,396
8151	Total hip replacement	0.80	16.03	22,893
4523	Colonoscopy	0.80	5.92	8,395
282	Tonsillectomy	0.79	2.85	4,017
7902	Closed fracture reduction of radius/ulna	0.77	1.89	2,578
602	Transurethral prostatectomy	0.74	8.59	11,307
8659	Skin suture NEC	0.71	2.24	2,848
863	Other local excision/destruction of skin and subcutaneous tissue	0.71	4.37	5,509
3859	Leg varicose vein ligation and stripping	0.62	2.76	3,030
4414	Closed endoscopic biopsy of stomach	0.62	6.71	7,342
5123	Laparoscopic cholecystectomy	0.53	6.11	5,735
283	Tonsillectomy/adenoidectomy	0.50	2.45	2,196
5302	Repair of indirect inguinal hernia	0.50	4.36	3,868
7935	Open reduction of fracture with internal fixation — femur	0.46	13.59	11,008
684	Total abdominal hysterectomy	0.45	9.50	7,666
0331	Spinal tap	0.45	5.33	4,263
5421	Laparoscopy	0.43	3.64	2,766
6902	D & C post delivery	0.41	2.28	1,641
4525	Closed endoscopic biopsy of larger intestine	0.35	8.00	5,033
8152	Partial hip replacement	0.33	14.68	8,482
4131	Bone marrow biopsy	0.32	10.33	5,838
3722	Left heart cardiac catheterization	0.30	7.48	4,025
All		77.04	5.58	765,135

Excludes 15 per cent of cases which had a Miscellaneous Diagnostic Procedure

TABLE 3.3B: TOP 30 PRINCIPAL PROCEDURES FOR NON-GMS PATIENTS, 1996

ICD-9-CM	Principal Procedure	Per Cent	LOS	Bed days
	No procedure	46.13	4.08	363,755
470	Appendectomy	2.16	4.59	19,177
741	Low cervical c-section	1.66	8.02	25,662
6902	D & C post delivery	1.56	1.77	5,339
282	Tonsillectomy	1.37	2.95	7,836
7902	Closed fracture reduction of radius/ulna	1.16	1.61	3,596
6909	D & C NEC	1.15	2.10	4,659
8659	Skin suture NEC	1.14	1.86	4,094
3859	Leg varicose v liga-strip	0.91	2.51	4,388
5732	Cystoscopy NEC	0.90	3.80	6,626
4516	Esophagogastroduodenoscopy with closed biopsy	0.88	6.66	11,275
0331	Spinal tap	0.83	5.07	8,153
283	Tonsillectomy/adenoidectomy	0.79	2.38	3,641
5123	Laparoscopic cholecystectomy	0.77	5.30	7,897
7936	Open reduction of fracture with internal fixation of the tibia/fibula	0.75	7.02	10,110
5421	Laparoscopy	0.70	2.95	3,983
684	Total abdominal hysterectomy	0.68	8.58	11,268
5302	Repair of indirect inguinal hernia	0.64	3.40	4,195
7534	Fetal monitoring NOS	0.64	3.60	4,424
863	Other local excision/destruction of lesion, tissue of skin and subcutaneous tissue	0.63	3.04	3,674
4413	Gastroscopy NEC	0.60	6.26	7,304
4523	Colonoscopy	0.59	5.48	6,237
4513	Small bowel endoscopy NEC	0.58	6.47	7,298
602	Transurethral prostatect	0.57	7.93	8,783
4414	Closed endoscopic biopsy of stomach	0.55	5.28	5,611
8151	Total hip replacement	0.52	15.14	15,143
8026	Knee arthroscopy	0.42	2.13	1,743
132	Linear extracapsular lens extraction	0.39	3.13	2,358
7935	Open reduction of fracture with internal fixation — femur	0.36	13.12	9,024
8604	Other incision and drainage of skin and subcutaneous tissue	0.35	4.56	3,112
All		70.36	4.27	580,365

Excludes 15 per cent of cases which had a Miscellaneous Diagnostic Procedure

TABLE 3.3C: TOP 30 PRINCIPAL PROCEDURES FOR GMS PATIENTS, 1997

ICD-9-CM	Principal Procedure	Per Cent	LOS	Bed Days
	No procedure	55.13	5.32	510,024
4516	Esophagogastroduodenoscopy with closed biopsy	1.34	8.12	18,842
5732	Cystoscopy NEC	1.23	4.52	9,684
470	Appendectomy	1.18	4.71	9,635
132	Linear extracapsular lens extraction	0.92	3.64	5,849
4413	Gastroscopy	0.88	7.50	11,403
6909	D & C NEC	0.87	2.24	3,380
1341	Phacoemulsification/aspiration of cataract	0.84	3.21	4,714
4523	Colonoscopy	0.83	6.21	8,923
8151	Total hip replacement	0.80	15.64	21,649
282	Tonsillectomy	0.78	2.83	3,850
8659	Skin suture NEC	0.73	2.27	2,858
4513	Small bowel endoscopy NEC	0.70	7.63	9,300
4414	Closed endoscopic biopsy of stomach	0.70	6.81	8,282
7902	Closed fracture reduction of radius/ulna	0.69	1.82	2,166
602	Transurethral prostatectomy	0.66	8.12	9,314
863	Other local excision/destruction of lesion, tissue of skin and subcutaneous tissue	0.66	4.24	4,830
5123	Laparoscopic cholecystectomy	0.57	5.86	5,808
7935	Open reduction of fracture with internal fixation — femur	0.56	12.99	12,575
3859	Leg varicose vein ligation and stripping	0.54	2.61	2,436
5302	Repair of indirect inguinal hernia	0.48	4.26	3,568
684	Total abdominal hysterectomy	0.47	9.21	7,478
741	Low cervical c- section	0.47	7.53	6,080
3722	Left heart cardiac catheterization	0.46	6.70	5,379
5421	Laparoscopy	0.45	3.80	2,995
6902	D & C post delivery	0.42	1.99	1,464
0331	Spinal tap	0.42	5.95	4,360
283	Tonsillectomy/adenoicectomy	0.42	2.60	1,885
8152	Partial hip replacement	0.38	13.91	9,233
7936	Open reduction of fracture with internal fixation of the tibia/fibula	0.38	7.08	4,692
All		74.93	5.47	712,656

Excludes 19 per cent of cases which had a Miscellaneous Diagnostic Procedure

TABLE 3.3D: TOP 30 PRINCIPAL PROCEDURES FOR NON-GMS PATIENTS, 1997

ICD-9-CM	Principal Procedure	Per Cent	LOS	Bed Days
	No procedure	43.99	3.88	332,089
470	Appendectomy	2.22	4.44	19,193
741	Low cervical c-section	2.02	7.74	30,433
6902	D & C post delivery	1.57	1.74	5,320
282	Tonsillectomy	1.31	2.98	7,574
7569	Repair of current obstetric laceration NEC	1.27	3.71	9,156
8659	Skin suture NEC	1.11	1.96	4,237
7902	Closed fracture reduction of radius/ulna	1.04	1.46	2,951
4516	Esophagogastroduodenoscopy with closed biopsy	1.03	6.83	13,735
6909	D & C NEC	1.03	1.98	3,970
5421	Laparoscopy	0.86	2.89	4,807
5732	Cystoscopy NEC	0.85	3.90	6,446
736	Episiotomy	0.85	4.06	6,662
3859	Leg varicose vein liagation and stripping	0.82	2.41	3,859
7936	Open reduction of fracture with internal fixation of the tibia/fibula	0.78	6.20	9,403
5123	Laparoscopic cholecystectomy	0.71	5.33	7,382
0331	Spinal tap	0.70	5.18	7,012
684	Total abdominal hysterectomy	0.68	8.54	11,264
283	Tonsillectomy/adenoidectomy	0.65	2.45	3,100
5302	Repair of indirect inguinal hernia	0.57	3.17	3,502
863	Other local excision/ destruction of lesion, tissue of skin and subcutaneous tissue	0.55	3.26	3,467
4414	Closed endoscopic biopsy of stomach	0.53	5.28	5,433
4413	Gastroscopy NEC	0.52	6.16	6,206
8151	Total hip replacement	0.51	14.98	14,766
602	Transurethral prostatectomy	0.50	7.57	7,380
4523	Colonoscopy	0.50	5.92	5,700
8622	Excisional debridement of wound, infection, or burn	0.48	4.49	4,220
4513	Small bowel endoscopy NEC	0.48	6.31	5,821
7301	Induction of labour by artifical rupture of membranes	0.46	3.99	3,596
3722	Left heart cardiac catheterization	0.46	6.37	5,732
All		69.06	4.13	554,416

Excludes 18 per cent of cases which had a Miscellaneous Diagnostic Procedure

3.5 Case-Mix by GMS Status

While interesting and useful, the presentation of information on diagnosis and procedures provides a one-dimensional perspective on the morbidity experience of discharges from the hospital system. To facilitate a multi-dimensional and therefore more informative assessment of morbidity, a measure of the case-mix, or patient mix, treated by the hospital may be applied. The Diagnosis Related Group (DRG) case-mix classification system has been adopted as the national standard by the Department of Health and Children since 1993 so this is the system adopted for analysis in this study. The DRG system is exclusive and exhaustive, meaning that all hospital discharges may be assigned to one and only one DRG. Within the DRG[3] system applied in this study there are around 495 DRGs in total and assignment is based on the patients' primary and secondary (if any) diagnoses, procedures performed, age, sex and discharge status. The first level of assignment is to the Major Diagnostic Category (MDC) which is broadly based on body system followed by assignment to the appropriate surgical or medical DRG within the relevant MDC. This section presents the results of the analysis of GMS and non-GMS discharges by MDC and DRG for 1996 and 1997.

In Table 3.4 we now look at the case-mix analysis presented by Major Diagnostic Category (MDC). We see that Disease and Disorders of the Digestive System (MDC 6) is the highest ranked MDC for both the GMS and non-GMS discharges for both years. For GMS discharges, the MDCs of the respiratory system, the circulatory system and the digestive system together account for over 40 per cent of all discharges in both 1996 and 1997. For the non-GMS group there is greater variation in the ranking of the MDCs between the two years though the expansion of the HIPE to include obstetrics is clearly in evidence for 1997.

---

[3] For hospital discharges in 1996 and 1997 the national standard adopted by the Department of Health and Children was Version 12.0 of the Health Care Financing Administration (HCFA) DRG system.

TABLE 3.4: PERCENTAGE DISTRIBUTION AND AVERAGE LENGTH OF STAY BY MAJOR DIANGOSTIC CATEGORY FOR GMS AND NON-GMS PATIENTS, 1996, 1997

MDC	Major Diagnostic Category	1996				1997			
		Per Cent		Length of Stay (days)		Per Cent		Length of Stay (days)	
		GMS	Non-GMS	GMS	Non-GMS	GMS	Non-GMS	GMS	Non-GMS
1	Diseases and disorders of nervous system	7.84	8.39	5.82	4.80	7.67	7.60	5.90	4.82
2	Diseases and disorders of the eye	3.41	2.14	3.92	3.65	3.14	1.95	3.82	3.60
3	Diseases and disorders of the ear, nose, mouth & throat	6.50	8.93	3.27	2.84	6.02	8.01	3.42	2.90
4	Diseases and disorders of the respiratory system	12.36	7.66	7.38	5.90	12.48	7.28	7.43	5.73
5	Diseases and disorders of the circulatory system	13.46	9.72	7.12	6.22	13.68	9.53	7.14	6.22
6	Diseases and disorders of the digestive system	14.60	14.11	5.57	4.60	14.19	13.58	5.55	4.51
7	Diseases and disorders of the hepatobiliary system & pancreas	2.50	2.31	7.43	6.29	2.69	2.25	7.44	6.46
8	Diseases and disorders of the musculoskeletal system & connective tissue	9.94	11.83	7.11	5.46	9.88	11.49	6.75	5.06
9	Diseases and disorders of the skin, subcutaneous tissue and breast	4.79	5.35	5.57	4.35	4.67	5.15	5.57	4.28
10	Endocrine, nutritional & metabolic diseases and disorders	1.89	1.52	7.25	6.15	1.90	1.46	6.87	5.88
11	Diseases and disorders of the kidney & urinary tract	4.45	3.75	6.11	5.14	4.44	3.67	6.14	4.89
12	Diseases and disorders of the male reproductive system	2.02	1.96	5.90	4.57	1.79	1.80	5.85	4.29
13	Diseases and disorders of the female reproductive system	3.51	4.40	4.79	4.44	3.47	4.36	4.84	4.27
14	Pregnancy, childbirth & the puerperium	1.85	7.41	3.80	4.11	3.50	12.13	3.47	3.88
15	New-borns and other neonates with conditions originating in the perinatal period	0.26	0.96	6.79	6.31	0.26	0.89	7.08	6.75

MDC	Major Diagnostic Category	1996				1997			
		Per Cent		Length of Stay (days)		Per Cent		Length of Stay (days)	
		GMS	Non-GMS	GMS	Non-GMS	GMS	Non-GMS	GMS	Non-GMS
16	Diseases and disorders of the blood and blood forming organs and immunological disorders	1.38	0.86	6.14	5.56	1.35	0.80	6.11	5.38
17	Myeloproliferative diseases and disorders, and poorly differentiated neoplasms	2.28	1.60	5.46	5.12	2.05	1.49	5.97	5.44
18	Infectious & parasitic diseases (systemic or unspecified sites)	1.60	2.14	4.82	3.94	1.52	1.89	5.16	4.17
19	Mental diseases & disorders	0.64	0.41	8.11	7.09	0.63	0.36	7.90	6.95
20	Alcohol/ drug use and alcohol/drug induced organic mental disorders	0.45	0.28	5.53	3.37	0.44	0.25	5.83	3.00
21	Injuries, poisoning & toxic effects of drugs	2.40	2.61	2.94	2.53	2.47	2.56	2.94	2.61
22	Burns	0.19	0.21	7.60	6.48	0.19	0.21	7.39	7.14
23	Factors influencing health status and other contacts with health services	1.44	1.19	5.44	3.37	1.29	1.08	5.04	3.07
24	Multiple significant trauma	0.06	0.16	8.50	9.58	0.07	0.16	10.74	9.76
25	Human immunodeficiency virus infections (HIV)	0.16	0.11	11.39	9.63	0.21	0.05	11.27	7.68
		100	100	5.98	4.80	100	100	5.96	4.67

In-patients with LOS 0-30 days

Tables 3.4a, b and c present the corresponding figures within specific age ranges, and show much closer correspondence between GMS and non-GMS patients within these age groups in terms of their distribution across MDCs. Table 3.4a focuses on those aged 0-14, and we see that for both GMS and non-GMS patients 3 MDCs account for about half of all discharges — MDC 3 (ear, nose, etc.), 4 (respiratory) and 6 (digestive). Table 3.4b focuses on those aged 15-64, where MDC 5 (circulatory) becomes important for both groups. MDC 5 is the highest ranked MDC in Table 3.4c which focuses on those aged 65 and over. Given the higher average age, it is interesting that for GMS discharges, conditions of the respiratory system (MDC 4) account for a greater proportion of discharges relative to the non-GMS group in this category. Length of stay variation is also clearly influenced by age and the morbidity experience for each category of GMS and non-GMS discharges analysed here.

The case-mix analysis now shifts to the DRG level in Tables 3.5a through 3.5d. For each group of discharges, the distribution across the top 30 high ranking DRGs are presented, together with the average length of stay and bed-days used. In addition, the Relative Value (RV) associated with each DRG for the relevant year (1996 and 1997) are presented. The DRG RV may be defined as the ratio of the average cost of treating a patient in a DRG relative to the average cost across all DRGs. An RV of 1 assumes, for example, that the average patient cost in the DRG equals that of treating the "standard" patient while a DRG with a RV of 2 is estimated to incur twice the average "standard" cost per discharge. For the purpose of applying a case-mix adjustment to the estimation of hospital budgets, the Department of Health and Children update estimates of the DRG RVs each year based on current hospital expenditure and activity data (Wiley, 1995). These will be centrally important in estimating in Chapter 4 the implications of differing case-mix for resource use. In order to give an indication of the differences between the DRGs in this respect, the tables also show the RVs estimated by the Department of Health and Children for 1996 and 1997 respectively.[4]

---

[4] As obsetric cases do not currently come within the scope of the Department's case-mix adjustment, RVs are not available for these DRGs.

TABLE 3.4A PERCENTAGE DISTRIBUTION AND AVERAGE LENGTH OF STAY BY MAJOR DIAGNOSTIC CATEGORY FOR GMS AND NON-GMS PATIENT: 1996, 1997 PATIENTS AGED 0-14

MDC	Major Diagnostic Category	1996				1997			
		Per Cent		Length of Stay (Days)		Per Cent		Length of Stay (Days)	
		GMS	Non-GMS	GMS	Non-GMS	GMS	Non-GMS	GMS	Non-GMS
1	Diseases and disorders of nervous system	8.75	8.66	2.90	2.81	8.10	8.19	2.89	2.69
2	Diseases and disorders of the eye	1.83	1.61	2.59	2.51	1.67	1.57	2.38	2.49
3	Diseases and disorders of the ear, nose, mouth & throat	19.53	18.36	2.55	2.24	17.86	17.06	2.56	2.26
4	Diseases and disorders of the respiratory system	13.74	12.55	3.97	3.17	14.24	13.05	3.93	3.25
5	Diseases and disorders of the circulatory system	1.23	1.39	4.42	4.80	1.28	1.44	4.13	5.06
6	Diseases and disorders of the digestive system	19.15	18.35	3.39	3.06	19.79	19.44	3.38	3.11
7	Diseases and disorders of the hepatobiliary system & pancreas	0.27	0.19	4.51	4.76	0.30	0.19	4.58	4.76
8	Diseases and disorders of the musculoskeletal system & connective tissue	7.95	9.13	3.18	2.86	8.44	9.78	2.93	2.74
9	Diseases and disorders of the skin, subcutaneous tissue and breast	5.01	5.13	2.98	2.35	5.55	5.36	2.75	2.44
10	Endocrine, nutritional & metabolic diseases and disorders	2.33	1.55	6.22	5.50	2.17	1.57	5.84	4.72
11	Diseases and disorders of the kidney & urinary tract	3.13	3.01	4.31	3.99	3.22	3.32	4.30	3.95
12	Diseases and disorders of the male reproductive system	2.39	2.45	2.03	2.03	2.16	2.31	1.98	1.99
13	Diseases and disorders of the female reproductive system	0.28	0.26	3.27	2.99	0.27	0.27	2.78	3.73
14	Pregnancy, childbirth & the puerperium	0.02	0.03	4.40	2.94	0.02	0.05	2.29	3.23
15	New-borns and other neonates with conditions originating in the perinatal period	1.52	4.32	6.86	6.31	1.65	4.32	7.11	6.76

MDC	Major Diagnostic Category	1996				1997			
		Per Cent		Length of Stay (Days)		Per Cent		Length of Stay (Days)	
		GMS	Non-GMS	GMS	Non-GMS	GMS	Non-GMS	GMS	Non-GMS
16	Diseases and disorders of the blood and blood forming organs and immunological disorders	0.98	1.02	3.94	3.73	0.97	0.91	3.63	3.49
17	Myeloproliferative diseases and disorders, and poorly differentiated neoplasms	1.31	0.83	3.89	4.87	1.48	0.74	3.81	4.04
18	Infectious & parasitic diseases (systemic or unspecified sites)	5.53	5.72	3.18	2.79	5.34	5.24	3.27	2.95
19	Mental diseases & disorders	0.45	0.47	4.97	4.59	0.49	0.39	5.01	4.63
20	Alcohol/drug use and alcohol/drug induced organic mental disorders	0.11	0.09	1.81	1.20	0.11	0.09	1.69	1.19
21	Injuries, poisoning & toxic effects of drugs	2.58	2.97	2.15	1.72	2.79	2.67	1.85	1.64
22	Burns	0.60	0.41	7.25	5.94	0.53	0.43	5.86	7.14
23	Factors influencing health status and other contacts with health services	1.25	1.44	2.83	2.48	1.52	1.54	3.08	2.72
24	Multiple significant trauma	0.04	0.07	6.92	8.15	0.05	0.05	11.41	8.50
25	Human immunodeficiency virus infections (HIV)	0.04	0.00	4.62	4.00	0.03	0.00	4.63	1.00
		100	100	3.33	3.02	100	100	3.29	3.07

In-patients with LOS 0-30 days

TABLE 3.4B: PERCENTAGE DISTRIBUTION AND AVERAGE LENGTH OF STAY BY MAJOR DIAGNOSTIC CATEGORY FOR GMS AND NON-GMS PATIENT: 1996 AND 1997 FOR PATIENTS AGED 15-64

MDC	Major Diagnostic Category	1996 Per Cent GMS	1996 Per Cent Non-GMS	1996 Length of Stay (Days) GMS	1996 Length of Stay (Days) Non-GMS	1997 Per Cent GMS	1997 Per Cent Non-GMS	1997 Length of Stay (Days) GMS	1997 Length of Stay (Days) Non-GMS
1	Diseases and disorders of nervous system	8.48	8.33	4.50	4.41	8.24	7.19	4.73	4.42
2	Diseases and disorders of the eye	1.79	1.69	4.02	3.93	1.58	1.49	3.98	3.85
3	Diseases and disorders of the ear, nose, mouth & throat	5.77	7.29	3.37	3.15	5.53	6.54	3.49	3.20
4	Diseases and disorders of the respiratory system	7.89	4.70	6.55	6.05	8.02	4.37	6.83	5.92
5	Diseases and disorders of the circulatory system	11.85	9.46	5.79	5.18	11.84	9.03	5.79	5.29
6	Diseases and disorders of the digestive system	14.50	13.08	4.84	4.49	13.60	12.16	4.77	4.40
7	Diseases and disorders of the hepatobiliary system & pancreas	3.15	2.91	6.17	5.71	3.27	2.69	6.32	5.92
8	Diseases and disorders of the musculoskeletal system & connective tissue	10.28	12.50	5.71	4.98	10.01	11.74	5.29	4.58
9	Diseases and disorders of the skin, subcutaneous tissue and breast	5.69	5.88	4.89	4.32	5.18	5.36	4.92	4.26
10	Endocrine, nutritional & metabolic diseases and disorders	1.80	1.47	6.31	5.71	1.87	1.33	6.04	5.60
11	Diseases and disorders of the kidney & urinary tract	4.29	3.67	5.26	4.81	4.00	3.44	5.43	4.49
12	Diseases and disorders of the male reproductive system	1.23	1.42	4.80	3.99	1.01	1.29	4.73	3.93
13	Diseases and disorders of the female reproductive system	7.04	6.72	4.27	4.32	6.56	6.37	4.31	4.11
14	Pregnancy, childbirth & the puerperium	4.50	12.06	3.79	4.11	8.15	18.94	3.47	3.88
15	New-borns and other neonates with conditions originating in the perinatal period	0.02	0.02	4.94	6.58	0.02	0.02	6.13	6.09

MDC	Major Diagnostic Category	1996				1997			
		Per Cent		Length of Stay (Days)		Per Cent		Length of Stay (Days)	
		GMS	Non-GMS	GMS	Non-GMS	GMS	Non-GMS	GMS	Non-GMS
16	Diseases and disorders of the blood and blood forming organs and immunological disorders	0.96	0.64	5.45	5.24	0.90	0.60	5.77	5.14
17	Myeloproliferative diseases and disorders, and poorly differentiated neoplasms	2.49	1.62	4.87	4.95	2.07	1.43	5.40	5.07
18	Infectious & parasitic diseases (systemic or unspecified sites)	1.05	1.27	5.58	5.00	1.00	1.12	5.62	5.25
19	Mental diseases & disorders	0.49	0.31	7.09	7.07	0.49	0.26	7.29	6.61
20	Alcohol/ drug use and alcohol/drug induced organic mental disorders	0.94	0.39	5.62	3.39	0.90	0.34	5.90	2.91
21	Injuries, poisoning & toxic effects of drugs	4.15	3.01	2.57	2.63	4.08	2.94	2.59	2.62
22	Burns	0.15	0.17	6.67	6.67	0.18	0.18	7.45	6.60
23	Factors influencing health status and other contacts with health services	1.02	1.01	3.75	2.81	0.91	0.91	3.88	2.56
24	Multiple significant trauma	0.10	0.21	8.42	9.63	0.11	0.20	10.76	9.97
25	Human immunodeficiency virus infections (HIV)	0.37	0.19	11.69	9.66	0.49	0.08	11.40	7.77
		100	100	5.01	4.54	100	100	4.99	4.39

In-patients with LOS 0-30 days

TABLE 3.4C: PERCENTAGE DISTRIBUTION AND AVERAGE LENGTH OF STAY BY MAJOR DIAGNOSTIC CATEGORY FOR GMS AND NON-GMS PATIENT: 1996 AND 1997 FOR PATIENTS AGED 65+

MDC	Major Diagnostic Category	1996				1997			
		Per Cent		Length of Stay (Days)		Per Cent		Length of Stay (Days)	
		GMS	Non-GMS	GMS	Non-GMS	GMS	Non-GMS	GMS	Non-GMS
1	Diseases and disorders of nervous system	6.87	8.26	8.83	8.92	6.93	8.53	8.58	8.81
2	Diseases and disorders of the eye	5.60	4.46	4.05	3.81	5.26	4.32	3.94	3.76
3	Diseases and disorders of the ear, nose, mouth & throat	2.17	2.67	5.48	5.13	2.29	2.37	5.64	5.37
4	Diseases and disorders of the respiratory system	16.14	12.12	8.89	9.34	16.40	11.67	8.81	9.02
5	Diseases and disorders of the circulatory system	19.74	21.47	7.96	8.01	20.01	21.99	8.03	7.87
6	Diseases and disorders of the digestive system	12.94	12.38	7.62	7.99	12.79	11.80	7.60	7.96
7	Diseases and disorders of the hepatobiliary system & pancreas	2.73	2.89	8.93	8.53	2.96	3.16	8.80	8.43
8	Diseases and disorders of the musculoskeletal system & connective tissue	10.39	12.93	9.61	9.55	10.27	12.62	9.33	9.19
9	Diseases and disorders of the skin, subcutaneous tissue and breast	3.83	3.74	7.85	8.15	3.84	3.98	7.93	7.55
10	Endocrine, nutritional & metabolic diseases and disorders	1.81	1.64	8.68	8.36	1.83	1.86	8.16	7.97
11	Diseases and disorders of the kidney & urinary tract	5.12	5.04	7.22	6.94	5.33	5.07	7.09	6.76
12	Diseases and disorders of the male reproductive system	2.65	3.30	7.75	7.91	2.45	3.23	7.54	7.01
13	Diseases and disorders of the female reproductive system	1.35	1.30	7.52	7.12	1.45	1.43	7.39	7.35
14	Pregnancy, childbirth & the puerperium	0.00	0.02	6.50	4.00	0.00	0.02	7.00	3.88
15	New-borns and other neonates with conditions originating in the perinatal period	0.00	0.01	4.00	3.50	1.94	0.01	6.72	7.00

MDC	Major Diagnostic Category	1996 Per Cent		1996 Length of Stay (Days)		1997 Per Cent		1997 Length of Stay (Days)	
		GMS	Non-GMS	GMS	Non-GMS	GMS	Non-GMS	GMS	Non-GMS
16	Diseases and disorders of the blood and blood forming organs and immunological disorders	1.94	1.43	6.91	7.77	2.24	1.49	7.03	7.24
17	Myeloproliferative diseases and disorders, and poorly differentiated neoplasms	2.45	2.52	6.36	5.61	0.68	2.69	9.82	6.73
18	Infectious & parasitic diseases (systemic or unspecified sites)	0.61	0.67	9.31	9.34	0.82	0.70	8.89	8.90
19	Mental diseases & disorders	0.86	0.70	9.29	9.28	0.10	0.73	6.80	9.05
20	Alcohol/drug use and alcohol/drug induced organic mental disorders	0.11	0.11	6.09	5.61	0.71	0.10	6.54	6.33
21	Injuries, poisoning & toxic effects of drugs	0.64	0.69	6.50	5.61	0.08	0.86	11.15	6.32
22	Burns	0.08	0.07	10.41	8.89	1.59	0.08	6.40	12.17
23	Factors influencing health status and other contacts with health services	1.92	1.51	6.97	5.83	0.05	1.20	10.46	5.24
24	Multiple significant trauma	0.04	0.09	9.39	10.56	0.00	0.09	7.50	8.74
25	Human immunodeficiency virus infections (HIV)	0.00		3.00		0.00	0.00		3.00

In-patients with LOS 0-30 days

In reviewing the information presented in Tables 3.5a-3.5d, greater homogeneity in the case-mix within each group of discharges is in evidence between the two years. For the GMS group, the top 30 DRGs account for close to 38 per cent of discharges in 1996 and 1997 and all but six of these DRGs are the same in both years. The 36 per cent of non-GMS discharges in the top 30 DRGs in 1996 increased to 38 per cent in 1997 and for this group all but three DRGs were the same in both years. Where high-ranking DRGs are common to both groups, the tendency for GMS patients to have relatively longer lengths of stay also holds true at this level.

The corresponding analysis for the three age categories 0-14, 15-64 and 65+ are presented in Appendix 2. The 30 high ranking DRGs account for around three-quarters of the discharges in the 0-14 group. There is greater dispersion among the adults and the elderly, however, as about one third of GMS discharges in the 15-64 group are concentrated among the high ranking DRGs compared with over 40 per cent of the non-GMS discharges. The analysis of the elderly discharges in Tables C3 and C4 shows that about half of those in the GMS group account for the top 30 DRGs compared with about 45 per cent of the non-GMS group. While this is not an epidemiological study concerned with the specifics of the conditions reported for each group of discharges, the integrity of the data are supported by the fact that the morbidity reflected by these reports is consistent with the age categories used for analysis.

Given the close relationship with older age, it is not surprising that conditions like lens procedures (DRG 39) and major joint and limb reattachment procedures including hip replacement (DRG 209) are found in the top 10 high ranking DRGs for elderly GMS and non-GMS discharges for both 1996 and 1997. As these procedures can be considered among the most common received by the elderly, a very cursory assessment shows that a similar proportion of each group receive these procedures. For those aged 65+, lens procedures accounted for around 3.2 per cent of all discharges nationally, 3.5 per cent of GMS discharges and 2.7 per cent of non-GMS discharges in 1997. Over three times as many of the GMS elderly received lens procedures compared with the non-GMS group, which is consistent with the fact that there are around two and a half times more discharges in the GMS 65+ group compared with the non-GMS group. The analysis of DRG 209, which includes hip replacement, shows that around twice as many GMS elderly were assigned to this group compared to the non-GMS elderly in 1997. The proportion of each group in this category is, however, rather similar as assignment to DRG 209 accounted for around 2.5 per cent of all elderly discharges, 2.3 per cent of GMS discharges and 2.9 per cent of non-GMS discharges. While there are similarities in the morbidity experience of GMS and non-GMS discharges in this age category, the resource implications of observed differences between the two groups in terms of factors like the age distribution and the utilisation of hospital services will be considered in the next chapter.

TABLE 3.5A: TOP 30 DRGs FOR GMS PATIENTS, 1996

DRG	Diagnosis Related Group	Total	Per Cent	LOS	Bed Days	RV96
183	Oesophagitis, gastroenteritis & miscellaneous digest disorders age >17 w/o cc	8,571	4.09	4.49	38,486	0.4718
88	Chronic obstructive pulmonary disease	6,563	3.13	8.31	54,557	1.0178
184	Oesophagitis, gastroenteritis & miscellaneous digest disorders age 0-17	5,511	2.63	3.13	17,257	0.4156
39	Lens procedures with or without vitrectomy	3,882	1.85	3.42	13,277	0.7312
127	Heart failure & shock	3,653	1.74	8.90	32,520	1.2575
140	Angina pectoris	3,490	1.67	6.50	22,698	0.8017
70	Otitis media & upper respiratory infection age 0-17	3,240	1.55	3.00	9,706	0.3929
98	Bronchitis & asthma age 0-17	3,056	1.46	3.45	10,551	0.4975
182	Oesophagitis, gastroenteritis & miscellaneous digest disorders age >17 with cc	2,827	1.35	6.77	19,149	0.8378
143	Chest pain	2,818	1.34	3.88	10,940	0.4449
89	Simple pneumonia & pleurisy age >17 with cc	2,726	1.30	9.40	25,632	1.3107
209	Major joint & limb re-attachment procedures of lower extremity	2,539	1.21	15.93	40,443	3.3112

DRG	Diagnosis Related Group	Total	Per Cent	LOS	Bed Days	RV96
14	Specific cerebrovascular disorders except TIA	2,532	1.21	10.85	27,463	1.9524
102	Other respiratory system diagnoses w/o cc	2,068	0.99	5.66	11,711	0.5845
25	Seizure & headache age >17 w/o cc	2,042	0.97	4.05	8,272	0.5789
243	Medical back problems	2,038	0.97	6.71	13,684	0.809
450	Poisoning & toxic effects of drugs age >17 w/o cc	1,869	0.89	2.25	4,210	0.3386
101	Other respiratory system diagnoses with cc	1,813	0.87	8.21	14,876	1.0653
395	Red blood cell disorders age >17	1,794	0.86	6.61	11,862	1.0509
410	Chemotherapy without acute leukaemia as secondary diagnosis	1,787	0.85	2.62	4,683	0.7645
422	Viral illness & fever of unknown origin age 0-17	1,769	0.84	2.64	4,678	0.3985
139	Cardiac arrhythmia & conduction disorders w/o cc	1,631	0.78	5.25	8,569	0.5675
167	Appendectomy w/o complicated principal diagnosis w/o cc	1,605	0.77	4.45	7,148	0.7168
60	Tonsillectomy &/or adenoidectomy only, age 0-17,	1,597	0.76	2.51	4,003	0.5371
364	D&C, conization except for malignancy	1,552	0.74	2.18	3,376	0.4958
15	Transient ischaemic attack & precerebral occlusions	1,551	0.74	7.03	10,902	0.8656
82	Respiratory neoplasms	1,450	0.69	9.22	13,372	1.4863
30	Traumatic stupor & coma, coma <1 hr age 0-17	1,432	0.68	1.68	2,412	0.2716
29	Traumatic stupor & coma, coma <1 hr age >17 w/o cc	1,364	0.65	2.54	3,470	0.3014
90	Simple pneumonia & pleurisy age >17 w/o cc	1,363	0.65	7.81	10,646	0.8191
		80,133	38.23	5.75	460,553	

In-patients with LOS 0-30 days.

TABLE 3.5B: TOP 30 DRGs FOR NON-GMS PATIENTS, 1996

DRG	Diagnosis Related Group	Total	Per Cent	LOS	Bed Days	RV96
183	Oesophagitis, gastroenteritis & miscellaneous digest disorders age >17 w/o cc	7,981	3.51	3.66	29,202	0.4718
184	Oesophagitis, gastroenteritis & miscellaneous digest disorders age 0-17	7,042	3.09	2.62	18,476	0.4156
98	Bronchitis & asthma age 0-17	4,135	1.82	2.86	11,823	0.4975
373	Vaginal delivery w/o complicating diagnoses	4,011	1.76	4.14	16,617	na
70	Otitis media & upper respiratory infection age 0-17	3,968	1.74	2.45	9,733	0.3929
167	Appendectomy w/o complicated principal diagnosis w/o cc	3,366	1.48	4.24	14,275	0.7168
371	Caesarean section w/o cc	3,048	1.34	7.91	24,116	na
381	Abortion with D&C, aspiration curettage or hysterectomy	2,820	1.24	1.73	4,885	na
143	Chest pain	2,682	1.18	3.41	9,148	0.4449
422	Viral illness & fever of unknown origin age 0-17	2,663	1.17	2.39	6,352	0.3985
359	Uterine & adnexa procedures for non-malignancy w/o cc	2,635	1.16	7.08	18,661	1.1657
243	Medical back problems	2,531	1.11	6.36	16,105	0.809
60	Tonsillectomy &/or adenoidectomy only, age 0-17	2,512	1.10	2.47	6,196	0.5371
383	Other antepartum diagnoses with medical complications	2,505	1.10	3.40	8,515	na
29	Traumatic stupor & coma, coma <1 hr age >17 w/o cc	2,444	1.07	2.08	5,072	0.3014
25	Seizure & headache age >17 w/o cc	2,347	1.03	3.75	8,811	0.5789
30	Traumatic stupor & coma, coma <1 hr age 0-17	2,292	1.01	1.52	3,482	0.2716
88	Chronic obstructive pulmonary disease	1,928	0.85	8.39	16,182	1.0178
119	Vein ligation & stripping	1,873	0.82	2.51	4,692	0.7191
364	D&C, conization except for malignancy	1,864	0.82	1.89	3,513	0.4958
140	Angina pectoris	1,768	0.78	6.25	11,049	0.8017
252	Fracture, sprain, strain & dislocation of forearm, hand, foot age 0-17	1,721	0.76	1.27	2,177	0.2485
139	Cardiac arrhythmia & conduction disorders w/o cc	1,687	0.74	4.31	7,268	0.5675

DRG	Diagnosis Related Group	Total	Per Cent	LOS	Bed Days	RV96
209	Major joint & limb re-attachment procedures of lower extremity	1,651	0.73	15.19	25,086	3.3112
162	Inguinal & femoral hernia procedures age >17 w/o cc	1,646	0.72	3.50	5,763	0.7078
69	Otitis media & upper respiratory infection age >17 w/o cc	1,643	0.72	3.36	5,521	0.4031
26	Seizure & headache age 0-17	1,635	0.72	2.75	4,499	0.52
450	Poisoning & toxic effects of drugs age >17 w/o cc	1,618	0.71	2.07	3,356	0.3386
278	Cellulitis age >17 w/o cc	1,615	0.71	4.62	7,458	0.5646
14	Specific cerebrovascular disorders except TIA	1,612	0.71	9.92	15,996	1.9524
		81,243	35.68	3.99	324,029	

In-patients with LOS 0-30 days

TABLE 3.5C: TOP 30 DRGS FOR GMS PATIENTS, 1997

DRG	Diagnosis Related Group	Total	Per Cent	LOS	Bed Days	RV97
183	Oesophagitis, gastroenteritis & miscellaneous digest disorders age >17 w/o cc	8,078	3.75	4.41	35,590	0.4620
88	Chronic obstructive pulmonary disease	7,059	3.27	8.24	58,158	1.0141
184	Oesophagitis, gastroenteritis & miscellaneous digest disorders age 0-17	5,345	2.48	3.12	16,677	0.4210
127	Heart failure & shock	3,646	1.69	9.04	32,945	1.2828
39	Lens procedures with or without vitrectomy	3,560	1.65	3.31	11,797	0.7247
140	Angina pectoris	3,280	1.52	6.26	20,545	0.7352
182	Oesophagitis, gastroenteritis & miscellaneous digest disorders age >17 with cc	3,156	1.46	6.65	20,979	0.8252
89	Simple pneumonia & pleurisy age >17 with cc	3,024	1.40	9.51	28,746	1.3071
98	Bronchitis & asthma age 0-17	3,002	1.39	3.63	10,908	0.4975
143	Chest pain	2,939	1.36	3.93	11,558	0.4546
70	Otitis media & upper respiratory infection age 0-17	2,917	1.35	2.93	8,540	0.4059
373	Vaginal delivery w/o complicating diagnoses	2,734	1.27	3.71	10,136	0.0000
209	Major joint & limb re-attachment procedures of lower extremity	2,530	1.17	15.53	39,282	3.1460

DRG	Diagnosis Related Group	Total	Per Cent	LOS	Bed Days	RV97
14	Specific cerebrovascular disorders except TIA	2,509	1.16	10.34	25,945	1.9779
102	Other respiratory system diagnoses w/o cc	2,030	0.94	5.22	10,601	0.5850
25	Seizure & headache age >17 w/o cc	1,977	0.92	3.90	7,701	0.5516
243	Medical back problems	1,950	0.90	6.36	12,396	0.7650
101	Other respiratory system diagnoses with cc	1,930	0.90	7.51	14,489	1.0344
450	Poisoning & toxic effects of drugs age >17 w/o cc	1,818	0.84	2.18	3,954	0.3441
395	Red blood cell disorders age >17	1,788	0.83	6.62	11,830	1.0363
15	Transient ischaemic attack & precerebral occlusions	1,722	0.80	6.79	11,694	0.8664
139	Cardiac arrhythmia & conduction disorders w/o cc	1,669	0.77	5.26	8,785	0.5751
167	Appendectomy w/o complicated principal diagnosis w/o cc	1,626	0.75	4.27	6,945	0.7077
422	Viral illness & fever of unknown origin age 0-17	1,530	0.71	2.54	3,890	0.4244
138	Cardiac arrhythmia & conduction disorders with cc	1,528	0.71	7.60	11,617	1.0349
122	Circulatory disorders with AMI w/o cardiovascular complication discharged alive	1,501	0.70	9.25	13,890	1.4488
383	Other antepartum diagnoses with medical complications	1,476	0.68	2.78	4,105	0.0000
294	Diabetes age >35	1,439	0.67	7.16	10,296	0.8337
359	Uterine & adnexa procedures for non-malignancy w/o cc	1,439	0.67	7.27	10,454	1.1261
60	Tonsillectomy &/or adenoidectomy only, age 0-17	1,426	0.66	2.54	3,618	0.5480
		80,628	37.39	5.93	478,071	

In-patients with LOS 0-30 days

TABLE 3.5D: TOP 30 DRGs FOR NON-GMS PATIENTS, 1997

DRG	Diagnosis Related Group	Total	Per Cent	LOS	Bed Days	RV97
373	Vaginal delivery w/o complicating diagnoses	12,126	5.14	3.92	47,488	n/a
183	Oesophagitis, gastroenteritis & miscellaneous digest disorders age >17 w/o cc	7,964	3.37	3.54	28,170	0.4620
184	Oesophagitis, gastroenteritis & miscellaneous digest disorders age 0-17	7,040	2.98	2.68	18,830	0.4210
98	Bronchitis & asthma age 0-17	3,967	1.68	2.87	11,368	0.4975
383	Other antepartum diagnoses with medical complications	3,786	1.60	3.15	11,923	0.0000
70	Otitis media & upper respiratory infections age 0-17	3,637	1.54	2.45	8,906	0.4059
371	Cesarean section w/o cc	3,553	1.51	7.57	26,908	0.0000
167	Appendectomy w/o complicated principal diagnosis w/o cc	3,467	1.47	4.14	14,362	0.7077
381	Abortion with D&C, aspiration curettage or hysterectomy	2,834	1.20	1.71	4,856	0.0000
359	Uterine & adnexa procedures for non-malignancy w/o cc	2,763	1.17	6.70	18,524	1.1261
143	Chest pain	2,672	1.13	3.33	8,890	0.4546
243	Medical back problems	2,458	1.04	6.04	14,844	0.7650
29	Traumatic stupor & coma, coma <1 hr age >17 w/o cc	2,412	1.02	2.25	5,430	0.3183
422	Viral illness & fever of unknown origin age 0-17	2,333	0.99	2.47	5,757	0.4244
60	Tonsillectomy &/or adenoidectomy only, age 0-17	2,306	0.98	2.50	5,762	0.5480
30	Traumatic stupor & coma, coma <1 hr age 0-17	2,201	0.93	1.60	3,529	0.2833
25	Seizure & headache age >17 w/o cc	2,131	0.90	3.51	7,473	0.5516
252	Fracture, sprain, strain & dislocation of forearm, hand, foot age 0-17	1,860	0.79	1.23	2,279	0.2445
88	Chronic obstructive pulmonary disease	1,710	0.72	8.10	13,848	1.0141
119	Vein ligation & stripping	1,697	0.72	2.37	4,014	0.7168
140	Angina pectoris	1,689	0.72	5.86	9,892	0.7352
384	Other antepartum diagnoses w/o medical complications	1,688	0.72	2.87	4,842	0.0000
139	Cardiac arrhythmia & conduction disorders w/o cc	1,660	0.70	4.18	6,934	0.5751

DRG	Diagnosis Related Group	Total	Per Cent	LOS	Bed Days	RV97
361	Laparoscopy & incisional tubal interruption	1,660	0.70	2.12	3,518	0.6086
278	Cellulitis age >17 w/o cc	1,650	0.70	4.54	7,483	0.5627
379	Threatened abortion	1,650	0.70	2.15	3,546	0.0000
209	Major joint & limb re-attachment procedures of lower extremity	1,629	0.69	14.87	24,218	3.1460
364	D&C, conization except for malignancy	1,625	0.69	1.86	3,023	0.5010
14	Specific cerebrovascular disorders except TIA	1,613	0.68	9.97	16,086	1.9779
69	Otitis media & upper respiratory infection age >17 w/o cc	1,599	0.68	3.43	5,479	0.4239
		89,380	37.86	3.90	348,182	

In-patients with LOS 0-30 days

3.6 Conclusions

To establish the balance between public and private workload in public hospitals, one has to take into account not only the number of patients treated but also the nature of the care provided to each group. The Hospital In-Patient Inquiry (HIPE), whereby public hospitals record and report on their activity levels, contains detailed information on the length of stay and nature of care provided to each patient. The data available for analysis in this study did not distinguish public from private patients, but it did allow those with and without medical card cover (GMS versus non-GMS) to be distinguished. About two-thirds of those not covered by a medical card have private health insurance. The differences in the extent and nature of utilisation of public hospital care between those with and without medical card cover — which are very interesting in their own right — thus also provides an indication of the differences between public and private patients.

We have seen in this chapter that in 1996 and 1997, GMS patients accounted for 44 per cent of the public hospital discharges reported through the HIPE. We also saw that patients with medical card cover are older and sicker and consume more bed-days than other patients. GMS patients accounted for about 54 per cent of all bed-days and had an average length of stay about 25 per cent longer than non-GMS patients. This was clearly related to the differing age profiles of the two groups, with the average age of GMS patients being almost 50 compared with only 38 for other patients. The highest concentration of GMS patients was among those over 65 years of age, whereas non-GMS patients were heavily concentrated in the 20-40 age range. This had major implications for both the nature of the conditions occurring in each group and the care provided. In particular, GMS patients were more likely to have been treated for a medical condition, and the non-GMS patients were more likely to have had a surgical procedure, when in hospital. Turning to case-mix as measured by the Diagnosis Related Group classification system, over 40 per cent of GMS patients were in the Major Diagnostic Categories relating to the respiratory system, the circulatory system and the digestive system, which was a higher degree of concentration than for non-GMS patients. Within DRGs, GMS patients tended to have longer average length of stay.

A classifier has now been introduced in the data reported by hospitals through HIPE allowing public and private patients to be distinguished. This represents a significant improvement in the data available to study the nature of public versus private care in public hospitals in the future. In this study, though, we now go on to explore the implications of the differences we have observed in the types of care provided to GMS and non-GMS patients for the resource use of these two groups, again serving as a proxy for differences between public and private patients.

Chapter 4

Public versus Private Resource Use in Public Hospitals and the Implications for Charges

4.1 Introduction

We have seen in the previous chapter that the HIPE data show GMS patients to be older and sicker and to spend more bed-days in public hospitals on average than non-GMS patients. What we are most interested in, however, in the current study is the resources used in providing private care in public hospitals. Still using the GMS/non-GMS distinction as the best proxy available to us of the public/private patient split, we focus in this chapter on the differences between these two groups in the cost of care provided. The data available allows us to see whether GMS patients receive types of care that are more costly on average than non-GMS patients: it does not allow us to see whether, within those care categories, one group actually receives more attention or consumes more resources than the other.

4.2 Measuring Resource Use

To measure resource use by different patients, we employ what is known as the Case Mix Index (CMI). The CMI is intended to reflect the relative costliness of the case mix, or patient mix, treated in a hospital. Estimation of the CMI for GMS and non-GMS discharges provides an indication of the relative resource intensity of treating each group of patients. For both 1996 and 1997, the overall CMI for GMS patients is in fact consistently higher than for the non-GMS group. The CMI for GMS patients was 0.95 in 1996 compared with 0.89 for non-GMS patients, indicating that the GMS patients were overall 6 per cent more resource intensive relative to non-GMS patients. The 2 per cent increase in the CMI for GMS patients to 0.97 in 1997 contrasts with a marginal decrease of just 1 per cent in the CMI for non-GMS patients to the 0.88 level in the same year. As the CMI measures the resource intensity of hospital workload, the lower CMI for non-GMS patients would suggest that this group of patients was less resource intensive relative to the GMS group.

However, this CMI differential between GMS and non-GMS patients needs to be seen in the light of the very different age profile of these two groups, as documented previously. Table 4.1 shows the case mix index by age group and by GMS status, and we see that when standardized for age, a different picture emerges. When compared with the GMS group, children and the elderly in the non-GMS group are more resource intensive while adults are relatively less resource intensive. The difference between the two groups is particularly striking for the elderly, with non-GMS discharges estimated to be close to 7 per cent more resource intensive relative to GMS patients.

TABLE 4.1: CASE-MIX INDEX BY AGE GROUPS FOR GMS AND NON-GMS DISCHARGES: 1996, 1997

	1996		1997	
	GMS	*Non-GMS*	*GMS*	*Non-GMS*
Children	0.60898	0.62523	0.61590	0.63437
Adults	0.91493	0.89629	0.92833	0.88686
Elderly	1.12619	1.19886	1.12996	1.19882
All Patients	0.95397	0.88679	0.96633	0.88373

This pattern carries through to Table 4.2, which attempts to estimate total expenditure on GMS and non-GMS discharges by age group for 1996 and 1997. For this purpose the Relative Value (RV) associated with each DRG, as described in the previous chapter, is employed. We saw that the RV for a DRG is the ratio of the average cost of treating a patient in that DRG to the average cost across all DRGs, estimated each year by the Department of Health and Children. The monetary valuation for an

RV unit is also updated annually by the Department of Health and Children, and the value of an RV unit was estimated at £1,318.14 in 1996 and £1,447.33 in 1997.

TABLE 4.2: RESOURCE INTENSITY OF GMS AND NON-GMS DISCHARGES FOR 1996 AND 1997, BY AGE GROUP

	Total RVs	Total Expenditure (£)	Bed-Days	Discharges	Exp./ Discharge (£)	Exp./ Bed-Day (£)
GMS 1996						
Children	21,421.72	28,236,826.00	114,850	34,453	819.58	245.86
Adults	75,891.37	100,035,450.45	430,909	86,045	1,162.59	232.15
Elderly	101,875.86	134,286,646.10	707,943	89,138	1,506.50	189.69
Total Discharges		262,558,922.55	1,253,702	209,636	1,252.45	209.43
Non-GMS 1996						
Children	31,848.91	41,981,322.23	150,220	32,493	845.14	279.47
Adults	111,516.45	146,994,293.4	634,368	92,475	1,051.94	231.72
Elderly	46,943.31	61,877,854.64	307,910	90,696	1,616.03	200.96
Total Discharges		250,853,470.3	1,092,498	215,664	1,101.68	229.61
GMS 1997						
Children	20,504.27	29,676,445.10	106,858	49,674	913.32	277.72
Adults	79,570.48	115,164,742.82	461,743	139,736	1,245.36	249.41
Elderly	104,334.09	151,005,858.48	715,699	38,290	1,664.97	210.99
Total Discharges		295,847,046.40	1,284,300	227,700	1,371.80	230.36
Non-GMS 1997						
Children	31,120.89	45,042,197.72	146,590	47,834	941.64	307.27
Adults	110,182.85	159,470,944.29	662,611	151,045	1,055.78	240.67
Elderly	45,698.61	66,140,969.21	292,863	37,205	1,777.74	225.84
Total Discharges		270,654,111.23	1,102,064	236,084	1,146.43	245.59

The total RVs presented in Table 4.2 represent the sum of RV units attributed to each DRG adjusted by volume. The total expenditure estimate by age group then results from the application of the appropriate monetary value for a relative value unit to the total relative value units attributed to each age category. Estimated expenditure by discharge and estimated expenditure by bed-day is determined for each group of discharges by dividing total discharges and total bed-days, respectively, by total expenditure for each age category.

The pattern of expenditure by discharge shown in Table 4.2 of course mirrors the variation by case mix index. When standardised for age, we see that children and the elderly in the non-GMS group are more resource intensive relative to the GMS group, while on the other hand GMS adults are slightly more resource intensive compared with non-GMS adults. Looking at the groups as a whole, however, for both 1996 and 1997 the GMS patients are shown, on average, to be more resource intensive per discharge, because their older age profile outweighs the fact that within two of the three age groups they are less expensive. The average cost of treating a GMS patient in 1997 is £1,372 while the corresponding figure for non-GMS patients is £1,146.

A rather different picture emerges when we look at expenditure per bed-day, however. For both 1996 and 1997, the non-GMS groups are more expensive in terms of expenditure per bed-day for both children and the elderly. For those in the 15-64 age group, there is little difference between GMS and non-GMS patients in 1996, while in 1997 GMS patients are more resource intensive. Overall, for both 1996 and 1997, non-GMS patients are shown to be more resource intensive per bed-day. The average cost per bed-day for GMS patients in 1997 is £230 while the corresponding figure for non-GMS patients is £246. Spending fewer days in hospital on average for each discharge, non-GMS patients have a higher cost per day though a lower cost per discharge. This is a key finding for the study, and we return in our final chapter (having studied the nature of demand for health insurance in some depth in the intervening chapters) to its implications for the level and structure of charges for private patients in public hospitals.

4.3 Care and Costs for Private versus Public Patients

If it could be assumed that GMS status is a reasonable proxy for public/private status, the information presented here from analysis of HIPE would suggest that private patients account for a lower proportion of bed-days than they do of discharges, which is consistent with the lower severity of case-mix in evidence for this group as a whole. GMS patients appear to be more resource-intensive relative to non-GMS patients in the acute inpatient environment in terms of each hospital spell. On a per-day basis, however, the opposite result was found: non-GMS patients cost more per day spent in hospital on average than GMS patients.

Having got to this point, two key issues arise. The first is whether GMS status can in fact serve as a reasonable proxy for public/private status: are the utilisation patterns of private versus public patients captured by the GMS/non-GMS comparison? The second issue arises because, even given data on private versus public patients, we would at present have no choice but to apply the average costs from the Department of Health's specialty costing estimates (from which the RVs employed above are derived) to both sets of patients. Is the assumption this would involve, of a common resource cost across public and private patients within specialties, valid? On both these issues further data was sought in the course of this study, though with rather limited success.

We were aware that data on public versus private workload, not reported in HIPE up to 1999, may nonetheless be gathered by many hospitals as part of their administrative recording systems. (The overall numbers of public and private patients is reported quarterly to the Department of Health and Children, as will be discussed in Chapter 7 below: here however we are interested in the nature and cost of the care provided.) The larger public hospitals were therefore approached in the course of the study to see, among other things, whether they could provide such data on public versus private utilisation, by for example DRG or the nature of care provided. Hospitals were also asked to provide information on any relevant cost data which may be available, differentiated by public/ private status. The Department of Health and Children provided a list of hospitals to be contacted, and wrote to them to seek their co-operation in the study, and the authors then wrote to the Chief Executive or hospital manager.

With some prompting from the Department, responses were eventually received from a majority of the hospitals approached. Many of these did have some information on private versus public utilisation, but this varied widely both in terms of information content and format. Effectively no information was available on expenditure distinguishing public versus private patients. In terms of care provided, in the time available it proved possible to obtain data distinguishing private from public patients and match it to the HIPE dataset for only two hospitals. While this was a disappointing outcome in terms of providing concrete input for the present study, it did initiate a process of consultation with hospitals which facilitated the introduction, in early 1999, of a new variable in the HIPE reporting system distinguishing private and public patients. This will significantly enhance the data available for analysis of private workload in public hospitals in the future.

The data we obtained from the two hospitals did allow us to see first the overlap between non-GMS and private patients in those hospitals. Table 4.3 shows first that about half the non-GMS patients in 1996 and 1997 were private patients and half were public: there were not pronounced differences in case-mix between these groups, though strong conclusions could not be supported by such a small number of cases. The table then shows the extent to which private patients were treated in designated private versus public beds in these two hospitals. We will be dealing with the bed designation system in detail in Chapter 7, but it is worth noting here that the balance between public and private beds does not match that between public and private patients. The additional data now being obtained in HIPE covers the public/private status of the patient, but not that of the bed in which they are treated, and we return in Chapter 7 to this data issue.

TABLE 4.3: DISTRIBUTION OF DISCHARGES BY GMS AND
PUBLIC/PRIVATE STATUS: RESULTS FOR TWO HOSPITALS

	Patient				Bed			
	1996		*1997*		*1996*		*1997*	
	GMS	*Non-GMS*	*GMS*	*Non-GMS*	*GMS*	*Non-GMS*	*GMS*	*Non-GMS*
Public	17,215	9,341	17,614	8,282	14,787	9,978	15,428	10,199
Private	589	8,073	663	9,096	1,144	5,476	1,214	5,220
Mixed					1,807	1,892	1,574	1,879
Non-Designated					66	68	61	80
Total	17,804		17,414	18,277	17,378	17,804	17,414	18,277	17,378

Returning finally to the issue of the overall cost of providing
private care in public hospitals, we have seen that about one in
five patients in public hospitals receives private care, and that
the likelihood is that this care is more costly on a per-night basis than the care received by public patients. Our GMS/non-
GMS comparison suggested that the differential in per-night
cost might be at least 7 per cent, and this seems likely to under-
state that difference if anything. About one-quarter of the direct
cost of providing in-patient care may then be attributable to
private patients. The expenditure figures presented in Table
4.2 above covered only the direct costs of providing care, and
came to about £520 million in 1996. This falls well short of total
expenditure on acute hospitals, which in 1996 was about twice
that figure. Concentrating on direct costs, however, these initial
estimates suggest that private care may have accounted for
about £130 million in expenditure on direct provision of care in
1996. This is a substantial figure, and amounts to about twice
the income from charges for private accommodation in that
year. Private patients are also subsidised through tax relief on
health insurance premia — which amounted to revenue forgone
of over £50 million in 1996 — and a proportion of this total can
also be seen as an effective subsidy on the cost of obtaining
private care in public hospitals.

4.4 The Implications for Charges

A key issue for this study is to assess, by reference to the costs associated with the delivery of private care in public hospitals, the likely effects of moving to full charging of the cost of provision for such private practice. Our analysis of HIPE data has shown that the average cost of care per day for non-GMS in-patients in 1997, based on their case-mix and on the Relative Value figures produced by the Department of Health and Children, was £246, compared with £230 for GMS patients. This figure, while quite tentative, provides a benchmark from which to assess the implications of the stated policy of moving towards charging full economic cost for private care in public hospitals.

It should be noted that the concept of "full economic cost" of private care is not unambiguous, and the appropriate basis for arriving at the charge one would actually wish to levy is also not simply determined by a costing exercise. First, the distinction between average and marginal cost is of course central. The argument for using average cost as the basis for charging for private care would be that it ensures that the cost of all the resources used in providing private care — in terms of staff, supplies, equipment and plant — is fully covered. However, this does not take into account the possible impact of private activity on the capacity of the system and thereby on average cost via economies or diseconomies of scale. The more appropriate basis for covering full cost may then be to focus on long-run marginal cost. This relates to all the *additional* costs associated with providing private care, taking into account not only the immediate direct costs, but also the longer-term impact of those higher activity levels on the hospital as a whole, including capital costs. Finally, even if these costs were accurately and comprehensively measured and one's objective was to recover them in full, that would not in itself determine the appropriate level of charging in a market environment. Decisions about charging for private care in public hospitals cannot but be influenced by the nature of that market, the availability, costs and charging policy of private care in private hospitals, and the nature of the health insurance market and the approaches adopted by insurers.

The information currently available relates to average costs (of non-GMS rather than private patients), and is not comprehensive in that the specialty costing exercise does not seek to incorporate all costs — such as, for example, costs of training. With the very limited information available, however, it is clear that the cost of provision of private care in public hospitals substantially exceeds the current level of charges for such care. At present, the per-night charge for a private bed in a public hospital is £171, while the corresponding figure for a semi-private bed is £134. Even given all the gaps we have highlighted in the information currently available, the cost of provision may be as much as twice the charge currently levied on a semi-private bed.

4.5 Conclusions

While preliminary and limited, this analysis of acute inpatients by GMS status shows important differences in case mix intensity for GMS and non-GMS patients. In summary, the data suggest that GMS patients are older and sicker, and consume more bed-days, than non-GMS patients but that non-GMS patients are more costly per day spent in hospital. In terms of the costs taken into account in the Department of Health and Children's specialty costing exercise, the average day spent in hospital by a non-GMS patient in 1997 cost £246, compared with £230 for GMS patients.

Two key issues then arise. The first is whether GMS status can in fact serve as a reasonable proxy for public/private status, and the second whether the average costs from the Department of Health's specialty costing estimates can reasonably be applied to both private and public patients. On both these issues extensive efforts to obtain further relevant information from public hospitals were made in the course of this study, but with limited success. This data-gathering exercise did however help to identify key gaps in the information regularly gathered for administrative and policy-making purposes, and provide a basis for assessing which might most readily be filled.

Even given all the gaps we have highlighted in the information currently available, the cost of provision may be as much as twice the charge currently levied on a semi-private bed. With about one in five patients in public hospitals receiving private care, and that care more costly on a per-night basis than the care received by public patients, about one-quarter of the direct cost of providing in-patient care may be attributable to private patients. The direct costs of providing care, taken into account in the costing exercise, fall well short of total expenditure on acute hospitals. Concentrating on direct costs, however, these initial estimates suggest that private patients may have accounted for about £120 million in expenditure on direct provision of care in 1996. This amounts to about twice the income from charges for private accommodation in that year, and private patients are also subsidised through tax relief on health insurance premia.

In the next two chapters we assess the implications of increased charges for private care in public hospitals for the demand for private insurance, the major mechanism through which the demand for private care itself would be affected.

Chapter 5

The Demand for Health Insurance

5.1 Introduction

A key aim of our analysis of private care in public hospitals and its resource implications up to this point has been to provide a better estimate of the cost of provision of that care than has been available heretofore. The stated intention of policy is to move towards charging the full cost of provision, and we have seen that this would involve a substantial increase in the level of charges for private care in public hospitals. Even given all the gaps we have highlighted in the information currently available, the cost of provision may be as much as twice the charge currently levied on a semi-private bed. For the purpose of illustration, suppose the level of charges for private and semi-private accommodation were both doubled. In broad terms, given the extent to which these charges currently contribute to the costs of the VHI in particular, an increase of this order of magnitude would be likely — *ceteris paribus* — to increase annual claims facing the VHI by one-quarter.[1] The next stage of our analysis is to assess the likely effect of such an increase on the demand for health insurance — a key factor in its effect on the overall demand for private care in public hospitals. Existing evidence on the responsiveness of demand for health insurance in Ireland to changes in price is rather limited, so for the pur-

---

[1] While recognising that the VHI is not the only insurer in the Irish market, it is by far the largest insurer and therefore provides the basis for illustrations put forward here.

pose of this study we undertook a variety of new analyses of the nature of the demand for health insurance in Ireland.

In this chapter we first analyse, in Section 5.2, the way in which the demand for health insurance has evolved over time in Ireland, and seek to relate this to factors one might expect to be important influences. We then present, in Section 5.3, results from an in-depth analysis of the characteristics of those who do and do not have health insurance. We use for this purpose data from the *Living in Ireland* household survey carried out by the ESRI in 1994. This is supplemented by more recent data from a follow-up survey in 1997, which is analysed in Section 5.4. In Chapter 6 we will go on to present results from a specially designed survey aimed at exploring attitudinal aspects of health insurance demand, carried out as part of this study.

5.2 The Evolution of Health Insurance Coverage in Ireland

Figure 5.1 shows the percentage of the population covered by health insurance from the VHI from 1960 to 1998. We see that this percentage has risen from only 4 per cent in 1960 to 39 per cent by 1998.[2] About 13 per cent were covered by the VHI by 1970, rising to about one-quarter by 1980 and holding at about 28-29 per cent through the early-mid-1980s. In 1987 growth picked up again (with an additional once-off increase due to new schemes to cover public hospital charges introduced at that time), and has continued through the 1990s. The advent of competition in the second half of the 1990s was an important change in the structure of the market, with the arrival of BUPA which now covers around 4 per cent of the population.

To try to identify the factors affecting the demand for health insurance we estimate a variety of time-series regression models, so first we discuss the explanatory variables one would like to include, the data actually available, and how key series evolved over the period. The obvious place to start is with the way the price of health insurance has moved over time. Data on

---

[2] The figures published by the VHI refer to the numbers insured in February of each year.

the level of premium increases is available from 1980, and from then to 1998 they cumulate to a nominal increase of 438 per cent. Over the 1980s, premia trebled, while from 1990 to 1998, premium increases amounted to 82 per cent. Over the whole period back to the early 1960s, though, the best proxy available for price is the average cost per person covered, calculated as total premium income divided by the numbers covered.[3] Unsurprisingly, the nominal amount increases enormously over the period, from about £3 per person in 1960 up to almost £200 by 1998. Deflating this by the increase in consumer prices, a very pronounced increase over the whole period is still seen: the real cost on average has increased more than 12-fold. Having increased by about 57 per cent during the 1960s, the average cost in real terms doubled over the 1970s, increased by about 270 per cent during the 1980s, and continued to rise rapidly during the 1990s.

FIGURE 5.1: VHI MEMBERSHIP AS PERCENTAGE OF TOTAL POPULATION

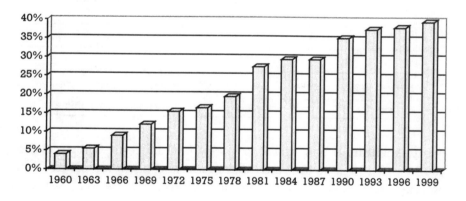

Figure 5.2 shows this price index from 1980, together with a measure of average income which one would of course also see as a key explanatory variable. For this purpose we use the an-

---

[3] This is not a true price measure, because it will be influenced by any changes in the composition of the insured population (as between adults and children) and their distribution over the different schemes on offer.

nual National Accounts aggregate personal disposable income, divided by the population.[4] We see that the price of VHI rose a good deal more rapidly than real incomes over the 1980s, reflecting both the relatively substantial increases in price and the stagnation in average income over much of that decade. In the 1990s, on the other hand, price and income have followed broadly similar trajectories. The fact that health insurance premia qualify for income tax relief further complicates the situation. The extent of this tax relief and its impact on the net cost of

Figure 5.2: Price of VHI Health Insurance, PD Income and Current Public Expenditure on Health in Real Terms (1990 = 100)

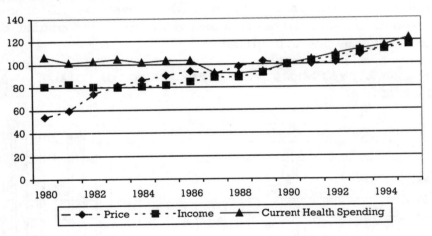

health insurance has varied over time. It increased during the 1970s and 1980s as tax rates increased and a higher proportion of taxpayers were drawn into the higher tax bands, but declined during the 1990s as rates were reduced and relief on health insurance premia — like other reliefs — was scaled back to apply only at the standard tax rate. The scale of the impact these changes could make can be simply illustrated. In the mid-1980s, the top tax rate was 60 per cent so someone facing that

---

[4] Changes in the composition of the population as between adults and children could affect the purchasing power implied, but year-to-year changes in the per capita measure seem a reasonable proxy.

rate and paying a premium of £100 bore a net cost of £40 for health insurance. By 1998 the standard tax rate was 24 per cent, and relief on £100 health insurance premium would leave the net cost at £76. Even if the gross price had not increased at all, then, the net cost would have risen almost doubled.

Apart from price and income, one might expect that a major influence on demand for health insurance in the Irish context would be perceptions of the health services available to those who do not buy health insurance. These certainly appear to play a role elsewhere, with for example studies of health insurance in the UK suggesting that the length of waiting lists facing public patients — actual or perceived — affect the demand for private care and private insurance (Besley et al., 1999). The difficulty lies in capturing these effects over time. Data on waiting lists exist only for very recent years. Data on overall public health expenditure are available, and Figure 5.2 also shows the evolution of public spending on health in real terms (deflated by the general deflator for current government purchases of goods and services). We see that from 1980 to the late 1990s this has been much flatter than either the price of insurance or incomes. During the first half of the 1990s public health expenditure kept pace with real incomes, but from 1996 a gap has been opening up as income growth accelerated. Supply-side factors affecting the availability of private care would also be expected to affect the attractiveness of health insurance, but are very difficult to track consistently over time. These would include not only the quantity and quality of private beds and facilities, but also the extent to which medical consultants are available to provide private care and, indeed, in a position to encourage patients to avail of that care or at a minimum make them aware of it.

In approaching the econometric modelling of health insurance demand in Ireland, the choice of explanatory variables is therefore heavily constrained by the nature of the data available. Without presenting here the detailed estimation results described in Harmon, Nestor and Nolan (1999), we can summarise the overall pattern. Focusing first on simple models incorporating only price and income as explanatory variables, two types of model were used. The first type analyses the variables in levels format, to try to explain the proportion insured in a given year by the levels of the explanatory variables in that and previous years. The fact that both the price and income time series are trending strongly upwards over the period makes it particularly difficult to distinguish their effects. Where the current level of price and income are included, all these variables are significantly different from zero, but a range of diagnostics tests suggest that the equation is severely misspecified, probably due to the omission of dynamic effects.[5] When the proportion insured in the previous period is introduced as an additional explanatory variable it is significantly different from zero, but the estimated coefficients are not consistent with a stable equilibrium.

Since heteroscedasticity appears to be a problem in these results, models expressing the variables in differences rather than levels were then estimated. These try to explain the change in the proportion insured between the previous period and this period, rather than the proportion insured itself — an approach often employed with strongly trended time-series. The estimated price effect is then significant and negative, while the proportion insured in the previous period is significant and positive. The results in effect show an upward trend in numbers insured from one year to the next, arising from factors not successfully identified in the model, but damped down somewhat by the negative effects of increases in price. For this equation serial correlation or misspecified dynamics still appear to be a problem, however, so the precise size of the estimated price effect cannot be regarded with much confidence. These results apply to gross price, whereas the reduction in tax relief should have contributed to a greater negative price effect on the demand for health insurance since about 1987. Such an effect was not evident in estimation when different sub-periods were distinguished: indeed, the impact of price was if anything more muted in the 1990s.

---

[5] Entering the ratio of price to income as explanatory variable, rather than price and income separately, did not alter this, nor did inclusion of a dummy variable for 1987, when as we have seen the numbers insured rose sharply due to special factors.

While data on additional variables was quite limited, as we have seen, we tested both current and capital public expenditure on health in our models but consistently failed to find significant effects. Data on number of beds in public acute hospitals was tried as an alternative measure (though it could mislead given the general trend internationally towards shorter lengths of stay), but also proved insignificant. These time-series results are at best suggestive, given unsatisfactory statistical aspects of the estimated equations and the fact that potentially important explanatory variables could not be included. Time-series analyses of health insurance for other countries have also emphasised the potential importance of variables which had to be omitted because they could not be measured adequately over time, notably availability and quality of care in the public system and supply-side influences on private care. Like those studies our results do suggest, however, that a negative effect of price increases on the demand for insurance in Ireland can be detected over the whole period in which insurance has operated.

5.3 Profile of Those with Health Insurance

These time-series results offer disappointingly little firm evidence on the factors underlying demand for health insurance in Ireland. We therefore turn to analysis of the characteristics of those who have insurance, using household survey data gathered by the ESRI in 1994. Unfortunately, by its nature such cross-section analysis can tell us little about the impact of price changes, which is a major interest here. However, identifying the distinguishing characteristics of those purchasing insurance should help to clarify the nature of demand for private health insurance in Ireland.

The 1994 *Living in Ireland Survey* is the first wave of the Irish element of the European Community Household Panel (ECHP) being carried out for Eurostat, the statistical office of the European communities, by the ESRI. This survey obtained information for 4,048 households, a response rate of 62.5 per cent of valid addresses contacted. The Electoral Register was the sampling frame and the responses were reweighted to accord with the Labour Force Survey in terms of key household characteristics. Results from this survey on household poverty have been published in Callan et al. (1996), which also contains a comprehensive description of the survey itself. The survey obtained detailed information on household and individual income and characteristics. It also asked each adult in responding households:

> "Are you medically insured (through VHI or any other health insurance company) either in your own name or through another family member?"

This allows the extent and nature of health insurance coverage to be studied. In addition, the survey contained questions about utilisation of health services in the previous year, and several questions relating to the health status of the respondent, in terms of self-assessed health and presence of chronic illness or disability.

Overall, 37 per cent of the adults in the 1994 *Living in Ireland* sample said they had health insurance, which is consistent with the level of coverage shown by administrative data. The survey allows a much richer set of characteristics to be examined than would be available from administrative data, covering not only age and gender but also for example income, occupation, social class and location. Note that the information about coverage is available only for adults, not for dependent children, and so the profile we present relates only to adults.

The proportion covered was very similar for men and women, and as a result about half the adults with health insurance are men and half are women. Table 5.1 shows that the proportion with health insurance first rises with age but peaks at 48 per cent for the 45-54 age range before falling to a relatively low figure of 22 per cent for those aged 65 or over. This means that about 37 per cent of the adults with insurance are aged under 35, 41 per cent are aged between 35 and 54, and only 22 per cent are aged 55 or over.

Table 5.2 categorises adults in the sample by the income position of the household in which they live. We see that the proportion with health insurance rises steadily as one moves up the household income distribution. The range is very wide, with coverage going from 8 per cent of those in the bottom decile (i.e. the bottom 10 per cent) of households up to 70 per cent of those in the top decile. This variation in coverage rates means that only 15 per cent of adults with health insurance are in the bottom half of the household income distribution, while almost half are in the top 20 per cent.

TABLE 5.1: HEALTH INSURANCE COVER BY AGE, 1994

Age	% with Health Insurance	% of Those with Health Insurance
Under 24	31.1	17.7
25-34	38.0	19.6
35-44	45.6	22.8
45-54	47.8	18.5
55-64	41.3	12.1
65 and over	22.1	9.4
All	37.2	100.0

TABLE 5.2: HEALTH INSURANCE COVER BY HOUSEHOLD INCOME, 1994

Income Decile	% with Health Insurance	% of Those with Health Insurance
Bottom	8.3	1.1
2	14.1	2.2
3	10.4	2.3
4	16.6	4.1
5	20.7	5.4
6	29.2	8.4
7	40.9	12.4
8	49.8	15.9
9	56.8	20.3
Top	69.9	27.9
All	37.2	100.0

Categorisation by household income takes no account of the fact that households differ in size and composition, and that this affects the living standards they can attain on a particular income level. One could calculate income per head to take this into account, but that represents an over-adjustment since it takes no account of economies of scale in consumption. The conventional approach to adjusting for these differences is therefore to calculate what is termed equivalent income, by dividing household income by the number of "equivalent" adults in the household. Various sets of equivalence scales can be used to derive the number of equivalent adults. Here we employ one widely used in the analysis of income inequality and poverty in Ireland, which attributes a vale of 1.0 to the first adult in each household, 0.66 to each additional adult, and 0.33 to each child. Table 5.3 then shows that the proportion of adults with health insurance is now slightly higher for the bottom than the second or third decile, but otherwise again rises as income rises and reaches 83 per cent for the top decile. About 17 per cent of adults with cover are now in the bottom half of the equivalent income distribution, while 41 per cent are in the top 20 per cent.

TABLE 5.3: HEALTH INSURANCE COVER BY HOUSEHOLD EQUIVALENT INCOME, 1994

Equivalent Income Decile	% with Health Insurance	% of Those with Health Insurance
Bottom	11.2	3.2
2	7.3	1.5
3	8.9	2.0
4	11.4	2.9
5	24.7	7.0
6	33.1	10.6
7	52.8	15.3
8	54.7	17.0
9	74.2	20.3
Top	83.2	20.3
All	37.2	100.0

Table 5.4 shows the relationship between health insurance coverage and social class, using the Central Statistics Office's sixth-class categorisation. Once again the proportion covered varies widely across the classes, going from as low as 9 per cent for the unskilled manual class up to 78 per cent for the higher professional and managerial one. Over half the adults with health insurance are in the top two classes, the higher and lower professional/managerial ones, while only 11 per cent are in the unskilled or semi-skilled manual classes.

TABLE 5.4: HEALTH INSURANCE COVER BY SOCIAL CLASS

Social Class	% with Health Insurance	% of Those with Health Insurance
Unskilled manual	8.9	3.3
Semi-skilled manual	19.1	8.0
Skilled manual	25.0	16.4
Intermediate non-manual	45.2	20.3
Lower professional/ managerial	69.4	20.7
Higher professional/ managerial	78.4	31.3
All	37.2	100.0

Table 5.5 focuses on the relationship between health insurance coverage and labour force status. The group with the highest proportion covered is the self-employed, at 63 per cent. Employees also have a relatively high coverage rate, at 53 per cent, and interestingly nearly half those in full-time education also have cover. Only about one-quarter of farmers are covered, and about the same proportion of those who are retired or working full-time in the home have health insurance. Less than one in ten of the unemployed or ill/disabled are covered. This pattern of coverage means that exactly half the adults with cover are employees, 19 per cent are working full-time in the home, and 10 per cent are in education.

TABLE 5.5: HEALTH INSURANCE COVER BY LABOUR FORCE STATUS

	% with Health Insurance	% of Those with Health Insurance
Employee	53.0	49.7
Self-employed	63.0	8.6
Farmer	27.0	3.8
Unemployed	6.3	1.5
Ill/disabled	9.8	0.7
Retired	27.2	6.9
Home duties	28.7	19.4
In education	47.8	9.7
All	37.2	100.0

Among employees, health insurance cover varies widely by occupation. Table 5.6 shows that almost two-thirds of clerical workers and 80 per cent of professionals are covered, with these two occupational groups accounting for half of the employees with insurance. By contrast only 10 per cent of labourers have health insurance, and these account for only 2 per cent of all those with cover.

TABLE 5.6: HEALTH INSURANCE COVER FOR EMPLOYEES BY OCCUPATION

Occupation	% with Health Insurance	% of Those with Health Insurance
Agricultural workers	24.7	2.7
Producers etc.	23.2	14.6
Labourers	10.0	2.0
Transport and comm.	31.0	5.2
Clerical	65.1	23.5
Commerce	43.1	14.1
Service	27.4	11.4
Professional	79.5	26.5
All	39.7	100.0

There is rather less variation among employees across industrial sectors, Table 5.7 showing that coverage ranges from 19 per cent in building and construction up to 60 per cent in professional services and 64 per cent in public administration and defence.

TABLE 5.7: HEALTH INSURANCE COVER FOR EMPLOYEES BY INDUSTRY

Industry	% with Health Insurance	% of Those with Health Insurance
Agriculture	24.3	6.4
Building and construction	18.7	3.5
Other production	30.7	19.0
Commerce and finance	49.3	21.2
Transport and comm.	52.8	7.5
Professional services	59.7	20.0
Public administration	63.9	8.9
Other	33.3	13.5
All	39.7	100.0

Returning to the full sample rather than just employees, Table 5.8 shows that married adults are a good deal more likely to have cover than single ones, with those who are separated, divorced or widowed having the lowest coverage rates. Almost two-thirds of those covered by insurance are married. Among married adults, insurance coverage rates vary little by presence and number of children, though families with four or more children have a relatively low proportion covered.

Private Practice in Irish Public Hospitals

TABLE 5.8: HEALTH INSURANCE COVER BY MARITAL STATUS

Marital Status	% with Health Insurance	% of Those with Health Insurance
Married	45.7	65.1
Separated/divorced/ widowed	17.6	4.7
Single	30.3	29.2
All	37.2	100.0

Health insurance cover increases markedly with education level attained. Table 5.9 shows that coverage rates go from 16 per cent for those with no qualification beyond primary up to 77 per cent for those with third-level qualifications. Nonetheless, 36 per cent of those with insurance cover do not have a Leaving Certificate or higher qualification.

TABLE 5.9: HEALTH INSURANCE COVER BY EDUCATION

	% with Health Insurance	% of Those with Health Insurance
No qualification beyond primary	15.5	15.3
Group/Inter/Junior Certificate	34.1	20.9
Leaving Certificate	51.1	38.2
Third level qualification	76.7	25.4
All	37.2	100.0

Table 5.10 shows how insurance cover varies by the type of area in which people live, going from "open country" to the largest urban conurbations. We see that coverage rates are lowest not in fully rural areas but in small towns, and highest in Dublin city. Over one-third of those with insurance are in Dublin city and county, but almost as many live in rural areas.

TABLE 5.10: HEALTH INSURANCE COVER BY LOCATION

	% with Health Insurance	% of Those with Health Insurance
Open country/village	31.3	34.7
Town < 5,000	27.7	5.5
Town > 5,000	38.9	14.2
Waterford, Galway, Limerick, Cork	43.4	9.9
Dublin city	45.8	28.7
Dublin county	42.6	6.8
All	37.2	100.0

Looking at insurance cover by tenure type, by far the highest coverage is for owner-occupiers without outstanding mortgages, with 61 per cent of that group having health insurance. The proportion of owner-occupiers with mortgages who have health insurance is very much lower at about one-third, but still higher than for those in private rented accommodation. Very few of those renting local authority housing have health insurance, though 15 per cent of those on local authority tenant-purchase schemes do have cover. In all, 97 per cent of those with cover are in owner-occupied housing (including tenant purchase).

Finally, we can look at the relationship between health insurance and public health care entitlement. About 57 per cent of those without medical card cover have private health insurance, compared with 4 per cent of those with medical card cover. Combining information on medical card cover and private health insurance, Figure 5.3 illustrates how private versus public cover varies by age and gender combined. As the number with private insurance rises with age, the number with no insurance falls, but the numbers with medical card cover rise only after retirement age. This pattern applies to men and women, although there would appear to be a higher proportion of men without cover from either source.

FIGURE 5.3: HEALTH INSURANCE COVER, 1994

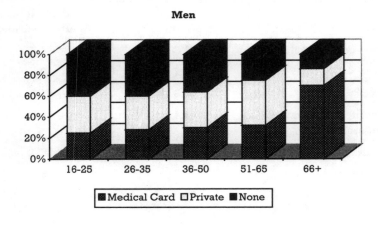

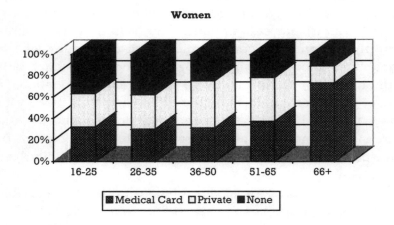

Those who choose to be privately insured may also be influenced by their own perception of their health state: there may be adverse selection into insurance of those more likely to need health care. A number of questions included in the 1994 survey obtained information about respondents' perception of their own state of health, and Table 5.11 looks at the reported health status of the individuals by whether they have private insurance, medical card cover, or neither. We see that the most striking finding is the dramatically higher proportion of those with medical card cover reporting low health states (which remains the case when men and women are examined separately). Those with private health insurance, by contrast, are more likely to report very good or good health than not only those with medical card cover but also those without that cover or health insurance.

TABLE 5.11: SELF-ASSESSED HEALTH STATUS BY INSURANCE COVERAGE

Health State	Very Good	Good	Fair	Bad	Very Bad
All	%	%	%	%	%
Private insurance	44.1	36.6	20.4	11.2	7.7
No insurance or medical card	33.8	31.3	21.9	18.3	3.1
Medical card	22.1	32.1	57.6	70.6	89.2

5.4 Regression Analysis of Choice of Private Insurance

The cross-tabulations presented in the previous section provide a detailed profile of those with health insurance, but we also want to home in on the key differences between those with versus those without health insurance, to identify the crucial factors affecting demand. For this purpose we need to estimate statistical models of the relationships involved, again using the 1994 *Living in Ireland* survey data. The estimation results presented here are taken from joint work with Dr. Colm Harmon of the Department of Economics, UCD, described in full in Harmon, Nestor and Nolan (1999).

The econometric analysis of the demand for private health insurance has developed a great deal in recent years (see, for example, Propper (1989a, b, 1998), Besley, Hall and Preston (1998, 1999), Cameron, Trivedi, Milne and Piggott (1988), Van de Ven (1987). A model proposed and applied to British data by Propper (1989b) takes the individual (or family) to be choosing simply whether to buy private insurance or not, and what is known in statistical terms as a probate model can be estimated. Table 5.12 shows the results from estimation of this model with the 1994 sample. The explanatory variables include a number of individual characteristics such as age, sex and marital status; household composition in terms of the number of children, adults and elderly persons; family income levels and health status variables. The table presents the estimated coefficients together with a statistic known as the z-ratio for a test of the null hypothesis of statistical insignificance.

Four different specifications of the model are estimated. Specification A includes only personal and household characteristics. The overall predicted probability of being privately insured on the basis of the mean values of the data is 35 per cent — very close to the actual figure in the sample. Education levels are highly significant determinants of the demand for insurance, higher levels of attainment increasing the probability of being insured. Being single lowers the probability of having private insurance. Looking at the household composition variables, the number of school-aged children, number of prime age adults and number of elderly individuals in the household are statistically significant, and all lower the probability of choosing private insurance.

In specification B the disposable income of the household is now included as an additional explanatory variable. Higher income is clearly associated with an increased probability of choosing private insurance, and the principal results in specification A remain.

In specification C we add to the model both the self-reported health status variables. In the case of a categorical variable one category has to be taken as the point of comparison and omitted from the equation. The omitted category in the case of self-reported health status is "Very Good" health. Responses that health was less good than that are all statistically significant and lower the probability of choosing private insurance — which does not suggest self-selection of those in poor health into insurance.

Finally, in specification D we include medical card status as an independent variable. Unsurprisingly this is strongly negatively associated with the demand for health insurance. It is important to note that the "pure" income effect is reduced dramatically when this is included, as is the scale of the negative effect of very poor health status.

TABLE 5.12: PROBIT MODEL OF DEMAND FOR PRIVATE HEALTH INSURANCE, IRELAND 1994

	(A)		(B)		(C)		(D)	
	coefficient	z ratio	coefficient	z ratio	coefficient	z ratio	coefficient	z ratio
Primary Cert	0.529	0.067	0.523	0.072	0.473	0.076	0.338	0.086
Some Secondary	0.690	0.068	0.652	0.074	0.606	0.078	0.494	0.087
Group Cert	0.949	0.079	0.936	0.083	0.850	0.088	0.664	0.097
Inter Cert	1.146	0.066	1.111	0.071	1.043	0.075	0.808	0.083
Junior Cert	1.945	0.097	1.816	0.126	1.753	0.133	1.459	0.145
Leaving Cert	1.788	0.063	1.744	0.068	1.659	0.072	1.337	0.080
PLC	1.665	0.108	1.668	0.116	1.574	0.122	1.253	0.131
Diploma	2.060	0.084	2.020	0.090	1.911	0.094	1.538	0.101
Degree	2.456	0.090	2.401	0.096	2.348	0.102	1.998	0.110
Higher Degree	2.519	0.116	2.475	0.124	2.376	0.128	2.000	0.135
Age	0.042	0.006	0.052	0.007	0.058	0.007	0.037	0.008
Age^2	0.000	0.000	0.000	0.000	0.000	0.000	0.000	0.000
Female	-0.084	0.029	0.006	0.036	-0.005	0.038	0.051	0.041
Single	-0.595	0.042	-0.626	0.044	-0.596	0.046	-0.448	0.051
Number School Children	-0.125	0.014	-0.124	0.015	-0.128	0.016	-0.059	0.018
Number Adults (16-64)	0.002	0.009	0.001	0.010	-0.003	0.011	-0.014	0.012

	(A)		(B)		(C)		(D)	
	coefficient	z ratio	coefficient	z ratio	coefficient	z ratio	Coefficient	z ratio
Number Elderly	-0.156	0.031	-0.149	0.034	-0.165	0.036	-0.131	0.039
Log Income	—	—	0.076	0.014	0.068	0.015	0.030	0.016
Good Health	—	—	—	—	-0.133	0.037	-0.111	0.040
Fair Health	—	—	—	—	-0.373	0.055	-0.202	0.062
Bad Health	—	—	—	—	-0.574	0.134	-0.214	0.149
Very Bad Health	—	—	—	—	-0.835	0.260	-0.185	0.297
Medical Card	—	—	—	—	—	—	-1.577	0.057
Constant	-2.099	0.167	-2.778	0.191	-2.709	0.202	-1.928	0.219
N	9365		8192		7393		7393	
Log Likelihood	-5051.18		-4278.13		-3821.99		-3311.04	

These results suggest that the demand for health insurance is strongly influenced by household income level, that age also has an influence, and that household composition might also impact on this choice. It also appears that self-reported health status and whether one is covered by a medical card also affect the probability of having insurance. Those covered by a medical card have a far higher chance of reporting themselves as in poor health than the non-insured. Even when one takes that relationship into account, however, both poor (self-reported) health and having medical card cover reduce the probability of having health insurance: there is no evidence in those terms of self-selection of those in poor health into insurance.

5.5 Evidence from the 1997 *Living in Ireland Survey*

Analysis of the 1994 *Living in Ireland Survey* has provided a detailed profile of those with private health insurance, and has allowed us to assess the distinguishing characteristics of those with insurance at that date. The numbers with private health insurance have continued to increase since that date, as the administrative statistics from the insurers show. The sample from the 1994 *Living in Ireland Survey* has been sought out for re-interview in each year since then, and the sample for 1997, the fourth wave of the panel survey, is now available for analysis. This panel data allows us to see who has become newly insured since 1994 — and if some of those who had insurance in 1994 are no longer insured by 1997. This is something which cannot be gleaned from published administrative statistics, but could be very important in interpreting trends in overall numbers insured and the way demand for health insurance has been evolving.

In each subsequent year, all individuals in the 1994 sample were followed up and household and individual interviews conducted again where possible, as long as the person still lived in a private household. The follow-up rules for the survey mean that new households might be included in each wave where a sample person from Wave 1 moved to another household. There has been considerable attrition between Waves 1 and 4, with only 63 per cent of the 14,585 individuals in the original sample still in completed Wave 4 households, with another 805 individuals having joined the sample at some point in the intervening years. However, in-depth checks have been made for any biases that could be introduced if attrition is related to characteristics of households, such as size, location, economic status and income. These checks suggest that the overall impact of attrition on the sample structure is slight.

The 1997 *Living in Ireland Survey* shows 39 per cent of adult respondents (interviewed in both waves) having private health insurance cover. The corresponding figure for these respondents in 1994 was 37 per cent, so the surveys do reflect the general increase seen in overall numbers insured over the period. However, we also find that there was some movement in and out of insurance between the two surveys underlying this net increase. About one-third of respondents were insured in both waves. However, 4 per cent of respondents were insured in 1994 but no longer insured by 1997; 5.5 per cent were not insured in 1994 but had become insured by 1997.

It is thus particularly interesting to compare the characteristics (in 1994) of these three distinct groups:

- Those who remained insured in both 1994 and 1997;

- Those who were not insured in 1994 but became insured by 1997; and

- Those who were insured in 1994 but were no longer insured by 1997.

Those who remained insured were evenly divided between men and women. However, men were over-represented among both those who became insured and those who became uninsured. Looking at age composition, Table 5.13 shows that those who remained insured are more heavily concentrated in the 35-54 age range than either of the other groups. Both those who became insured and those who became uninsured have a substantially higher proportion aged under 24. Those who became insured also have the highest proportion in the older 55-64 age range, whereas those who became uninsured have the highest proportion in the 25-34 age range. This pattern is consistent with movement from being insured to being uninsured occurring when for example a student, covered on their parents' policy, moves out of education into work, or when a young person covered on such a policy moves out of the parental home. Movement into insurance, on the other hand, may also occur when moving into work, and some tendency to become insured in the pre-retirement decade is also plausible.

TABLE 5.13: HEALTH INSURANCE STATUS IN 1994 AND 1997 BY AGE, ADULTS IN *LIVING IN IRELAND SURVEYS*

Age in 1994	Insured in Both Waves	Insured in 1997, Not in 1994	Insured in 1994, Not in 1997
	%	%	%
Under 24	12.7	25.0	29.2
25-34	19.3	16.4	23.2
35-44	27.0	19.8	17.5
45-54	20.5	11.9	14.2
55-64	10.8	18.2	7.5
65 and over	9.7	8.8	8.5
All	100.0	100.0	100.0

Table 5.14 shows that both those who became insured and those who became uninsured were a good deal more heavily concentrated in the bottom half of the distribution than those who remained insured. About 29 per cent of those who became insured and 29 per cent of those who became uninsured, compared with 15 per cent of those who remained insured, were in households in the bottom half. By contrast, almost half those remaining insured were in the top two deciles, compared with only one-third of those who became insured and 29 per cent of those who became uninsured.

TABLE 5.14: HEALTH INSURANCE STATUS IN 1994 AND 1997 BY HOUSEHOLD INCOME, ADULTS IN *LIVING IN IRELAND* SURVEYS

Income Decile in 1994	Insured in Both Waves	Insured in 1997, Not in 1994	Insured in 1994, Not in 1997
	%	%	%
Bottom	0.8	3.1	3.1
2	2.2	4.4	4.6
3	2.4	5.6	3.5
4	3.4	10.3	7.0
5	6.0	5.3	10.1
6	7.7	17.5	11.5
7	12.8	12.6	16.7
8	17.3	8.5	14.1
9	21.5	15.1	10.3
Top	26.0	17.6	19.0
All	100.0	100.0	100.0

Those who remained insured are also more concentrated in the higher social classes than the other two groups. Table 5.15 shows that only one-quarter of those who remained insured are in households headed by someone in the manual social classes, compared with 54 per cent of those who became insured and 48 per cent of those who became uninsured. This clearly reflects the spread of health insurance beyond its traditional base in the higher social classes.

Focusing on labour force status, Table 5.16 shows that just over half those who remained insured are employees, but the corresponding figure for those who became insured is only 40 per cent. We see that a relatively high proportion of those who became insured were in full-time education in 1994. Examination of their labour force status in 1997 (not shown) reveals that most of these individuals had indeed left full-time education and become employees by then. The same applies to the smaller numbers unemployed or ill in 1994 who became insured by 1997. The group who became uninsured by 1997 look more like those who remained insured, though a higher proportion are farmers and some of those who were employees in 1994 had moved into unemployment, illness, retirement or home duties by 1997.

TABLE 5.15: HEALTH INSURANCE STATUS IN 1994 AND 1997 BY SOCIAL CLASS, ADULTS IN *LIVING IN IRELAND SURVEYS*

Social Class in 1994	Insured in both waves	Insured in 1997, Not in 1994	Insured in 1994, Not in 1997
	%	%	%
Unskilled manual	4.7	12.2	10.6
Semi-skilled manual	13.2	24.0	19.4
Skilled manual	8.5	17.4	18.5
Intermediate non-manual	28.9	27.6	25.4
Lower professional/ managerial	25.4	13.2	15.2
Higher professional/ managerial	19.3	5.6	10.9
All	100.0	100.0	100.0

TABLE 5.16: HEALTH INSURANCE STATUS IN 1994 AND 1997 BY LABOUR FORCE STATUS, ADULTS IN *LIVING IN IRELAND SURVEYS*

Labour Force Status in 1994	Insured in Both Waves	Insured in 1997, Not in 1994	Insured in 1994, Not in 1997
	%	%	%
Employee	51.8	39.8	48.5
Self-employed	7.9	6.7	6.7
Farmer	3.4	7.0	7.2
Unemployed	1.1	3.5	3.2
Ill/disabled	0.2	2.6	0.6
Retired	7.3	5.3	5.3
Home duties	21.1	20.4	18.3
In education	7.0	14.5	9.9
All	100	100	100

Table 5.17 shows that almost three-quarters of those who remained insured were married, considerably more than for the other two groups. A relatively high proportion of those who became uninsured were separated, divorced or widowed.

TABLE 5.17: HEALTH INSURANCE STATUS IN 1994 AND 1997 BY MARITAL STATUS, ADULTS IN *LIVING IN IRELAND SURVEYS*

Marital Status in 1994	Insured in Both Waves	Insured in 1997, Not in 1994	Insured in 1994, Not in 1997
	%	%	%
Married/cohabiting	73.2	56.6	50.5
Separated/divorced/Widowed	4.6	2.5	8.6
Single	22.2	40.9	40.9

Finally, Table 5.18 looks at tenure type. It shows that owner-occupiers without outstanding mortgages were most likely to remain insured. The proportion of owner-occupiers with mortgages is higher for both those who became insured and those who became uninsured. Those on local authority tenant-purchase schemes also comprise a relatively high proportion of both those groups, but particularly those who became insured.

TABLE 5.18: HEALTH INSURANCE STATUS IN 1994 AND 1997 BY TENURE, ADULTS IN *LIVING IN IRELAND SURVEYS*

Tenure in 1994	Insured in Both Waves	Insured in 1997, Not in 1994	Insured in 1994, Not in 1997
	%	%	%
Owner-occupied with mortgage	34.9	43.4	42.4
Owner-occupied without mortgage	58.7	37.6	41.6
Local Authority tenant-purchase	3.7	14.5	9.2
Local Authority rented	0.4	3.4	3.6
Private rented	2.3	1.0	3.0
All	100.0	100.0	100.0

The final, and important, finding from the comparison of the 1994 and 1997 *Living in Ireland Surveys* relates not to the coverage of health insurance but to who is paying for that cover. In 1994, only about 3 per cent of the adults with health insurance cover were having the cost of that insurance partially or fully met by their employer. By 1997, this had risen to 6 per cent. This is consistent with other evidence that employers, particularly in the rapidly growing multinational sector, are increasingly interested in providing this type of benefit in order to attract and retain highly skilled staff. Increasing employer provision would in itself be expected to reduce the sensitivity of the overall demand for health insurance to either straightforward price increases or further diminution in tax relief on premia.

5.5 Conclusions

The numbers covered by health insurance have grown dramatically over time in Ireland, reaching over 40 per cent of the population by the end of the 1990s. This growth has produced a radical transformation in the setting in which private provision in public hospitals — the focus of this study — operates. This chapter has examined the evolution of the numbers insured over time, before turning to in-depth examination of the characteristics of those who have versus those who do not have insurance, making use of household survey data gathered by the ESRI in 1994 and 1997.

The time-series analysis on how coverage of health insurance has evolved in Ireland attempted to see if key influences — particularly that of price — could be identified. The results were at best to be seen as suggestive, given unsatisfactory statistical aspects of the estimated equations and the fact that potentially important explanatory variables relating to perceptions of the public health service could not be included. Like similar studies elsewhere, they do suggest that a negative effect of price increases on the demand for insurance in Ireland can be detected over the whole period in which insurance has operated, serving to damp down what would otherwise have been an even more pronounced upward trend. Reductions in tax relief should have contributed to a greater negative price effect on the demand for health insurance over the past decade, but that was not evident in the results.

The detailed profile of adults with private health insurance showed that very similar numbers of men and women were covered, that coverage was highest in the 35-54 age range, and that married people were more likely than single adults to have cover. Coverage rose markedly with household income, but about 17 per cent of those covered were in the bottom half of the household income distribution, and a significant minority at the top of that distribution did not have cover. Coverage was highest for the professional/managerial social classes, though significant numbers in the manual social classes had cover. The proportion with cover was particularly high for the self-employed, while among employees those in clerical and professional occupations were most likely to have cover. Coverage was higher in Dublin than elsewhere, and lowest in small towns and rural areas. Those with private health insurance tended to report better health than people without insurance, whereas those with medical card cover reported worse health than the rest of the sample.

To try to disentangle the influence of different characteristics, the results of econometric analysis of the demand for health insurance in the 1994 sample were presented, drawing on joint work with Colm Harmon. Estimated models of the probability of having health insurance showed that education level attained, household income, age and marital status were all significant predictors of that probability. Incorporating the measures of self-reported health suggested that, controlling for other characteristics, poor health made one less rather than more likely to have insurance: there was no evidence of adverse selection, though one would ideally like further measures of health status to test this comprehensively. Those with medical card cover were unsurprisingly much less likely than others to have insurance, even after controlling for other characteristics including household income levels.

The 1997 *Living in Ireland Survey*, which followed up those interviewed in 1994, was used to compare those who had health insurance at both dates with those who moved in or out of insurance coverage. The numbers with health insurance had increased in the 1997 sample compared with 1994, but there was some movement out of as well as into insurance between the two surveys. About one-third of respondents were insured in both waves, 4 per cent were insured in 1994 but not by 1997, and 5.5 per cent were not insured in 1994 but had become insured by 1997. Those who remained insured were more heavily concentrated in the 35-54 age range than those moving into or out of insurance, and also rather more heavily concentrated in the top half of the income distribution, in the professional/ managerial social classes, and in owner-occupied housing. The numbers having the cost of health insurance met by their employers also increased between the two surveys, a trend which could have a significant impact on the sensitivity of demand to price increases.

Chapter 6

Attitudes to Health Insurance

6.1 Introduction

The analysis in the previous chapter of the growth in health insurance found it difficult to measure some of the factors that may affect demand over time, notably perceptions of the state of the public health care system. Its profile of those with health insurance and what distinguishes them from the rest of the population, while highly suggestive, could not of course reveal precisely why these people buy health insurance. To try to probe precisely what it is that health insurance is seen as "buying", and whether it is seen as still good value for money, a special survey module was designed and included as part of a regular survey carried out by the ESRI in early 1999. In this chapter we report the results from that survey, and assess their implications for the nature of the demand for health insurance in Ireland.

6.2 The Data

The ESRI carries out a regular monthly Consumer Survey by telephone, with a sample size in each round of about 1,250, designed to be nationally representative. The Consumer Survey itself obtains information about subjective evaluations of the state of the economy, consumer confidence, spending plans etc., together with some classificatory variables such as occupation and broad income range. Additional modules can be attached to this survey, and in the January and February 1999 rounds a specially designed module on health insurance was included for the purpose of the present study. Responses were obtained from 2,620 individuals in total.

The health module first asked a series of questions about the respondent's health status, drawn from the SF12 health status measurement instrument widely employed in the UK. It then asked whether the respondent has private health insurance, and those who said they did were asked questions tapping:

- What they regarded as the most important reasons for having health insurance;

- Whether they regarded the cost of health insurance as good value and how they would react to an increase;

- What would concern them about the public hospital system if they did not have insurance;

- Whether they personally know someone who has recently had a lengthy wait for public hospital treatment, whether they think waiting times have got longer, and how long they think is acceptable waiting time in specific circumstances.

Respondents who said they do not have health insurance were asked:

- Whether they have considered taking out insurance;

- Why they might do so;

- How much difference a reduction in the price of insurance might make;

- Whether they personally know someone who has recently had a lengthy wait for public hospital treatment, whether they think waiting times have got longer, and how long they think is acceptable waiting time in specific circumstances;

- How much difference lengthening waiting times might make to their views about insurance.

All respondents, whether they had insurance or not, were also asked about their utilisation of different health services in the past twelve months, including waiting times. A range of information on the characteristics of respondents and their house-holds was also obtained, including age range, gender, occupa-tion, education and household income range. We now turn to the results, beginning in the next section with those who had insurance.

6.3 Responses of the Insured

About 43 per cent of those who responded to the survey said that they did have private health insurance. Of these, over 8 per cent said that the cost of this health insurance was paid by an employer, reflecting the rapid growth in the provision of this benefit by employers in recent years.

A list of eight possible reasons for having health insurance was then put to those with insurance, that set being drawn from previous research on this topic described in Nolan (1991). Re-spondents were asked to say whether they regarded each as very important, quite important or not at all important as a rea-son for having private medical insurance. The responses are summarised in Table 6.1. We see that "being sure of getting into hospital" and "fear of large medical or hospital bill" are nominated as very important by 86-88 per cent of those with insurance, and almost everyone with insurance regards these as either very or quite important. However, "being sure of get-ting good treatment in hospital" is also regarded as very im-portant by more than three-quarters of those with insurance, and again as very or quite important by almost all the insured. Being sure of getting consultant care and being able to arrange the timing of hospital treatment are seen as very important by more than two-thirds of the insured. By contrast, being able to have a private or semi-private room and being able to get into private hospitals are seen as very important by only about one-quarter of the insured. Respondents were given the option of volunteering other reasons for having cover, and these gener-ally related to the need for financial security, the desirability of having cover for the family, and waiting times and quality of care.

TABLE 6.1: REASONS FOR HAVING HEALTH INSURANCE

Reason	% Saying Very Important	% Saying Very or Quite Important
Being able to have a private or semi-private room in hospital	27.8	65.2
Being able to choose your own consultant	52.7	88.9
Being sure of getting into hospital quickly when you need treatment	86.4	98.6
Being sure of getting good treatment in hospital	77.4	95.9
Being able to get into private hospitals	27.2	63.3
Being sure of getting consultant care	67.5	96.0
Being able to arrange hospital treatment for when it suits you	68.7	95.7
Fear of large medical or hospital bills	88.5	98.4

Looking at the way responses to this question varied across respondents, we find that those regarding "being sure of getting into hospital" as a very important reason look very much like the insured as a whole — not surprisingly, since this response was given by the vast majority of the insured. The same was true of, for example, "being sure of getting good treatment in hospital". It is only where the reason in question was regarded as very important by only a minority of the insured that we begin to see some variation across characteristics. For example, those who regarded "being able to have a private or semi-private room" as very important were marginally more likely to be older, female, married, and retired or in home duties than those not giving this response. Even there, though, the differences are not pronounced.

It is worth noting that this pattern of responses differs in some important respects from that found by a similar exercise carried out to inform *inter alia* assessment of the impact of changing the entitlement structure in 1991, reported in Nolan (1991). Respondents to three rounds of the Consumer Survey (which was not then a telephone survey) were given a similar list of options and asked which they regarded as the most important, the next most important, and the least important reason for having health insurance. The results in that case were absolutely dominated by "being sure of getting into hospital quickly when you need treatment": 77 per cent of respondents regarded this as the most important or next-most important reason for having insurance. The other suggested reasons were very much less important, with for example "being sure of getting consultant care" regarded as most or next-most important by 24 per cent, and the corresponding figure for "being sure of getting good treatment" was 36 per cent. Differences between the 1991 and 1999 surveys in the precise format of the question and the mode of administration have to be kept in mind. These results do nonetheless suggest that while access has remained a key reason for having health insurance, issues relating to quality of care have become somewhat more important over the 1990s in attitudes towards insurance.

The next question was whether respondents regarded the price of their current health insurance as quite cheap, good value, expensive, very expensive or close to unaffordable. We see from Table 6.2 that while very few regard the price of insurance as quite cheap, 35 per cent regard it as good value, 43 per cent regard it as expensive, but only 18 per cent regard it as very expensive and very few say it is close to unaffordable. Those regarding the current price as very expensive or close to unaffordable comprised more older respondents than those not giving those responses, as well as more retired or in home duties. They also were drawn less often from the top income range employed in the survey: about 30 per cent had household income of £360 or more per week, compared with 36 per cent for the insured as a whole.

TABLE 6.2: ATTITUDES OF THE INSURED TO THE COST OF HEALTH INSURANCE

Regard Price of Health Insurance as:	%
Quite cheap	1.6
Good value	35.0
Expensive	43.1
Very expensive	17.7
Close to unaffordable	2.6

Probing attitudes to the price of insurance further, respondents were asked how they would be likely to respond to an increase in price. First, if price went up next year by 10 per cent, how likely are they to give it up entirely — on a five-point scale from very likely to most unlikely. We see from Table 6.3 that only 8 per cent of those with insurance thought such a price increase — similar to the scale of actual increases in premia in some recent years — would be sufficient to make it very likely that they would give up insurance. Only 22 per cent thought it was at all likely. If the increase was 20 per cent, the percentage saying "very likely" was still 8 per cent, though there was some increase in the numbers responding "quite likely" or "likely". However, when a 50 per cent increase in price was postulated, one-quarter of those with insurance said it was very likely that they would give it up, and 56 per cent regarded it as either very likely, quite likely or likely.

TABLE 6.3: RESPONSES OF THE INSURED TO AN INCREASE IN THE COST OF HEALTH INSURANCE

Give up Insurance if Price:	Very Likely	Very or Quite Likely	Very or Quite or Likely
	%	%	%
Rose 10%	7.8	14.6	21.7
Rose 20%	8.2	19.0	33.5
Rose 50%	25.5	36.5	55.6

While such subjective responses are not always a good predictor of behaviour, they do suggest that an increase in price of the order of 10 per cent in a given year would not in itself be enough to discourage most of those currently insured from continuing cover. There was relatively little variation in these responses by age, occupation or household income, though those most likely to give up insurance in response to a 50 per cent increase in price were self-employed rather than professional/managerial employees, and the elderly were least likely to do so.

The insured were then asked what would most concern them about having to rely on the public hospital system if they had to give up insurance — quality of care, possible length of time waiting for treatment, or lack of privacy. When given this choice three-quarters said that it was possible length of time waiting for treatment that would concern them most, 22 per cent said quality of care, and only 3 per cent said lack of privacy. This is consistent with the general pattern displayed in Table 6.1, with concern about waiting times uppermost in people's minds, quality of care also now a significant issue, and privacy not seen as important. The small group nominating lack of privacy as their main concern were disproportionately elderly, female and from the highest income category.

Given the extent of concern about waiting times, it is important to know more about the basis on which people's perceptions are being formed about the actual situation in this regard. The insured were therefore asked, "Do you yourself personally know any family, friends or neighbours who have recently had lengthy waits for public hospital treatment?" Just under half — 46 per cent — said that they did, while 54 per cent responded in the negative. When asked whether they thought waiting times for treatment in public hospitals are longer now than 5 years ago, almost two-thirds of the insured — 65 per cent — said they did, 28 per cent said they did not, and the remainder did not know. A question then asked what respondents would regard as the maximum acceptable waiting time for a 65-year old to have to wait for a hip replacement operation to relieve pain and increase mobility. Almost half said a wait of 4 weeks or less was acceptable, 96 per cent said 6 months or less.

6.4 Responses of Those Without Private Health Insurance

We now turn to the attitudes of the majority of respondents to the survey who did not have health insurance — also clearly an important part of the context in which decisions about health insurance are taken. These respondents were first asked whether they had ever seriously considered taking out private health insurance, and one-quarter said that they had. These were a distinctive sub-group in terms of age, marital status, employment, education and income. Almost 80 per cent were aged under 50, compared with 64 per cent for the uninsured as a whole, and 60 per cent compared with 47 per cent were married. About 56 per cent were full-time employees compared with 36 per cent for the uninsured as a whole, a significantly higher proportion had a Leaving Certificate or higher qualification, and 57 per cent were in the top two income ranges compared with 37 per cent for the uninsured as a whole.

Those without insurance were then asked what would be the main reason for seriously considering taking out private health insurance, and given a choice once again between quality of care, possible length of time waiting for treatment, and lack of privacy. In a pattern very similar to the responses of the insured, 70 per cent said possible waiting time was the most important reason, 27 per cent said quality of care was the most important, and only 3 per cent said lack of privacy.

When asked about the impact of a fall of 10 per cent in the price of insurance, 23 per cent of those without insurance thought they would then be very likely to take it out, while a total of 52 per cent said they would be very or quite likely to do so.

When asked whether they knew anyone who had recently experienced a lengthy wait for hospital treatment, 49 per cent of those without insurance said they had — marginally higher than the corresponding percentage for those with insurance, which we saw was 46 per cent. When asked whether they thought waiting times for treatment in public hospitals are longer now than 5 years ago, the same pattern was found — 68 per cent of those without insurance (compared to 65 per cent of the insured) said they did, 24 per cent said they did not, and the remainder did not know. When asked what they would regard as the maximum acceptable waiting time for a 65-year old to have to wait for a hip replacement operation to relieve pain and increase mobility, about half those without insurance said 4 weeks or less, 96 per cent said 6 months or less — very much the same as the responses of the insured.

Finally, those without private health insurance were asked about the likely impact of lengthening waiting lists in the future. The precise question was "If waiting times for public hospitals were to get longer in the future, do you think that that, of itself, would make you much more likely to buy private health insurance (given your current income and the current cost of insurance)?" One-third said that this was very likely, while 46 per cent said it was likely, 14 per cent said it was unlikely and 7 per cent responded "not at all".

6.5 Actual Waiting Times for Hospital Care

All respondents — both insured and uninsured — were also asked about their own recent experiences of health services utilisation. Table 6.4 summarises the responses in terms of numbers receiving treatment and waiting times. We see that about 13 per cent had an in-patient stay in the past year, and 64 per cent of these said that they did not have to wait for admission. This presumably represents for the most part admissions through accident and emergency departments, though it could also include elective admissions of private patients at pre-arranged times. Of those who did have a wait, three-quarters said they had to wait for four weeks or less, and only 8 per cent said they waited for more than 12 weeks. About 58 per cent of those with insurance who had a hospital stay said they did not have to wait for admission, compared with 69 per cent of those without insurance. This may of course reflect the greater probability of being admitted through accident/emergency for the latter, on the basis of their older age profile and higher morbidity levels. For those who said they did wait for admission, length of wait was broadly similar for the insured and uninsured.

TABLE 6.4: HOSPITAL SERVICES UTILISATION AND WAITING TIMES, 1999 SURVEY

	In-patient	Casualty	Out-patient	Day Surgery
	%	%	%	%
% availing of service	12.9	11.8	16.7	3.7
% of these having waited	35.6	n/a	31.9	37.7
Length of wait for these:				
4 weeks or less	74.0		59.4	38.5
5-12 weeks	18.0		26.9	28.4
13-26 weeks	5.1		6.4	22.4
27-52 weeks	3.1		7.3	10.7

As far as hospital outpatient services are concerned, 9 per cent of respondents had visited a casualty department at least once in the previous 12 months and 17 per cent had visited an outpatient clinic. About 68 per cent of those who visited an outpatient clinic said they did not have to wait to get this treatment; of those who had to wait, about 60 per cent waited for 4 weeks or less, and 14 per cent waited for longer than 12 weeks. Only 20 per cent of the insured who visited an out-patient clinic, compared with 38 per cent of those without insurance, said they had to wait.

Turning to day surgery, 4 per cent of respondents visited hospital for such surgery in the previous 12 months. Of these, 38 per cent said they had to go on a waiting list for this treatment. Of those who had to wait, 38 per cent waited for 4 weeks or less, but about one-third waited for more than 12 weeks. About 33 per cent of the insured, compared with 43 per cent of those without insurance, who had day surgery said they had to go on a waiting list.

Finally, respondents were also asked whether they were themselves currently on a waiting list for in-patient treatment, and 3 per cent said that they were. When asked how long they had been on the waiting list, one-fifth of these said 4 weeks or less, 37 per cent said between 5 and 26 weeks, 22 per cent said between 27 weeks and one year, and 20 per cent said more than a year. While it was a good deal more common for those without insurance, it is worth noting that some of the insured were waiting: 4.6 per cent of those without insurance versus 1.4 per cent of the insured said they were currently on a waiting list for in-patient treatment. Of those who said they were on a waiting list, none of the insured had waited for more than a year, whereas 22 per cent of those without insurance had done so.

6.6 Implications for the Sensitivity of Demand for Health Insurance in Ireland

We have seen from earlier chapters that the cost of provision of private care in public hospitals may be as much as twice the charge currently levied on a semi-private bed, and that a doubling in the level of charges for private accommodation would be likely — *ceteris paribus* — to increase annual claims facing the VHI by about one-quarter. Drawing on the results presented in this and the previous chapter, what impact would this be likely to have on the numbers purchasing health insurance?

If such an increase in charges was implemented all at once, and if it were to be carried through to an immediate increase of that scale in the level of premia, it would represent a substantial increase by historical standards. The evidence from other countries, from our analysis of Irish experience, and from attitudinal responses, suggest that this would be sufficient to have a noticeable impact, reducing the numbers purchasing health insurance. However, a continuation of the policy of recent years of phased increases from year to year, moving towards the higher level of charges over a lengthy period of years, would have rather less impact. One could, for example, envisage increased charges leading to an additional increase — over and above the rate of increase arising for other reasons — of under 5 per cent per year for five years. Recent experience suggests that the forces leading to increasing demand for health insurance in the Irish case are powerful. Both attitudinal responses and this experience suggest that annual increases in the cost of insurance in excess of those recently seen, while they might indeed be enough to cause the rate of increase in numbers insured to tail off for a time, would not be enough in themselves to produce a dramatic reduction in the numbers insured.

This is of course dependent on those forces promoting demand for insurance continuing to operate. While it is difficult to be certain, it seems probable that two key influences are economic growth and perceptions of the alternative to private care — namely the care available to public patients. Economic growth appears set to continue at a healthy, if somewhat slower, rate over the next decade: if it does not, and in particular if the level of investment and job creation by the multinational sector fell away sharply, then the implications of price increases for the demand for insurance could be very different.

The prospects for perceptions of the care available to public patients are if anything even harder to assess. They will of course depend on the quality and availability of that care, and on indicators available to the public such as waiting lists, but the picture conveyed in the media is also relevant. Some interesting UK research is attempting to measure not just the impact of indicators such as waiting lists, but also the nature of media stories, on public perceptions of the NHS and consequently on attitudes to health insurance — an area that as yet remains unexplored in the Irish context. The evidence presented in this chapter brought out however that waiting times are indeed the main concern people have about relying on the public hospital system, but quality of care was also a significant issue. The public health system clearly faces a major challenge in improving perceptions of the service it provides.

6.7 Conclusions

To probe why people buy health insurance, a special survey module was designed and included as part of the regular monthly Consumer Survey carried out by the ESRI. The module was carried in the January and February 1999 rounds of the survey, and responses were obtained from 2,620 individuals in total. About 43 per cent of respondents said they had health insurance. When asked about reasons for having health insurance, almost all said being sure of getting into hospital was an important reason. However, being sure of getting good treatment, being sure of getting consultant care, and fear of large hospital bills were also very widely regarded as important. Compared with the pattern of responses from a similar exercise carried out in 1991, this suggests that while access has remained a key reason for having health insurance, issues relating to quality of care may have become somewhat more important over the 1990s.

Those with insurance appeared relatively insensitive to a price increase next year of the order of 10-20 per cent, though over one-third said they would be very likely to give up insurance if the price went up by 50 per cent. When asked what would concern them most about relying on the public hospital system, waiting times were the main concern, but quality of care was also a significant issue, with privacy not regarded as important. Almost half the insured said they personally knew someone who had recently had a lengthy wait for public hospital treatment, and two-thirds believed that waiting times for treatment in public hospitals were longer now than 5 years ago.

Those without health insurance in the survey had very similar patterns of response to the insured, in terms of reasons for now considering having health insurance, perceptions of public waiting lists, and what was acceptable in terms of waiting times. About one-third said that, if waiting times for public hospitals were to get longer in the future, it would make them much more likely to buy health insurance.

Respondents were also asked about their own recent utilisation of health services, including waiting times. About 13 per cent had an in-patient stay in the past year, of whom almost two-thirds said they did not have to wait for admission. Of those who did have to wait, only 8 per cent waited for more than 12 weeks: interestingly, reported length of wait was similar for those with and without insurance — though such an overall comparison does not take differences in age and health status between the two groups into account. About two-thirds of those who visited an outpatient department did not have to wait: of those who did have to wait, 14 per cent waited for longer than 12 weeks. The uninsured were a good deal more likely than the insured to have visited an out-patient clinic. About 3 per cent of respondents said they were currently on a waiting list for in-patient treatment: 20 per cent of these had been waiting for more than a year. While it was a good deal more common for those without insurance, some respondents with insurance were waiting for in-patient treatment.

Chapter 7

Access of Private Patients to Public Hospitals

7.1 Introduction

Concern about equity of access led to the introduction in the early 1990s of new arrangements for access to care for public versus private patients in public hospitals. This includes a "bed designation" system, whereby most beds in public hospitals have been designated as for public or private use. In order to assess these arrangements in terms of ensuring equity in access, as set out in the Health Strategy (Department of Health, 1994), one would wish to empirically examine their effects. We have sought to do so in this study both by analysis of available data and by seeking new data. We begin by describing the arrangements and then consider the extent to which their operations can be assessed with existing data. We also briefly consider the related issue of waiting times for hospital care for public versus private patients. Finally, we summarise the conclusions and highlight data needs in terms of monitoring and evaluating the arrangements and assessing equity of access.

7.2 The Bed Designation System and Public/Private Bed Use in Public Hospitals

The background to the introduction of the bed designation and associated monitoring system has already been described in Chapters 1 and 2. To recap briefly, certain features of the system of access to public hospitals as it operated in the late 1980s were widely seen as militating against the proper operation of the principle of equity. This was reflected for example in the Report of the Commission on Health Funding, which recommended the introduction of a common waiting list for public and private patients awaiting planned admission to public hospitals, from which cases would be taken in the order of medically established priority. Rather than this approach — which would face a number of problems — in 1991 the Programme for Economic and Social Progress ushered in several related changes designed to promote equity.

Entitlement Category III, which gave limited entitlement to the top 15 per cent of the population in terms of coverage for hospital care, was abolished, placing all those without medical card cover on an equal footing in terms of public entitlements. Secondly, new arrangements for admission to public wards in public hospitals were introduced with the stated aim of arriving at a situation whereby private patients availing of public hospitals for elective (non-emergency) treatment would eventually be accommodated only in private or semi-private beds. Following discussions with hospital and Health Board management as well as the medical organisations, most acute beds in public hospitals were designated by the Department of Health as either public or private. Legislative underpinnings were provided by the 1991 Health (Amendment) Act. The number of beds initially designated as public and as private and the manner in which the public/private stock evolved during the 1990s has been described in Chapter 2. We saw that about 20 per cent of in-patient beds in acute public hospitals are currently designated as being for private patient use, while about 32 per cent of day beds are so designated.

Our focus in this chapter is on the use of these beds, as between public and private patients. On a phased basis over a period of three years from 1991, hospitals were to introduce systems to restrict access of private patients to public beds, and reporting mechanisms to allow bed use to be monitored by the Department were also introduced. For the purpose of these arrangements, the definition of private status is that the patient is opting to avail of private consultant services, rather than public consultant services available to everyone. Someone could have health insurance but opt to be treated as a public patient, while not everyone opting to avail of private consultant services need have insurance. In terms of implementing the arrangements, hospitals were instructed that a patient being admitted arising from a private out-patient consultation is presumed to be a private patient, unless the patient specifies to the contrary and this is confirmed in writing by the consultant. Patients admitted through accident/emergency departments may opt at the time of admission or subsequently to have private status. Those opting for private status are to be accommodated in a private or semi-private bed if one is available (and the patient's condition does not require them to be in, for example, non-designated intensive care). If a private bed is not available, a private patient may occupy a public bed provided that the consultant certifies that an emergency admission is required. Similar certification is in principle required if it is necessary to admit a public patient through emergency and accommodate them in a private bed. For elective admissions, separate waiting lists for public and private beds are entailed.

The extent to which designated public versus private beds are occupied by public versus private patients is reported by hospitals to the Department of Health and Children on a quarterly basis, as part of a monitoring system set up in tandem with the bed designation exercise. Data for 1995-1997 have been provided to us by the Department. These data are taken from what is termed the (Eligibility Arrangements) EA04 form returns made by hospitals to the Department. It was this source which allowed us to document in Chapter 2 that the proportion of all bed-days spent in public hospitals accounted for by private patients rose from 18 per cent in 1995 to 21 per cent in 1997, with private patients accounting for about the same proportion of day bed use.

Rather than the overall numbers of private patients, what we now want to concentrate on is the extent to which these patients were actually accommodated in private or semi-private beds. There are some gaps in the coverage of the reporting system in this respect, including unavailability of full data from one major hospital, so the totals reported here differ slightly from those in

Chapter 2, but this should not affect the overall pattern. Table 7.1 shows the number of bed-days reported to have been spent by private patients in designated public beds and vice versa. (A small number of bed-days are in beds not designated as either public or private.) This shows that the number of bed-days spent by private patients in designated public beds rose over the period, from 115,000 in 1995 up to 159,000 in 1997. This represented a very substantial proportion — almost one-quarter — of all the bed-days spent by private patients in public hospitals. A smaller but still substantial absolute number of bed-days was spent by public patients in designated private beds — almost 116,000 in 1997. This represented almost 5 per cent of all the bed-days spent by public patients in public hospitals.

TABLE 7.1: PUBLIC VERSUS PRIVATE BED USAGE IN PUBLIC HOSPITALS* (EXCLUDING DAY BEDS), 1997

	Total Bed Days Used by Public Patients	Total Bed Days Used by Private Patients	Private Bed-Days in Public Beds	Public Bed-Days in Private Beds
1995	2,542,680	574,214	125,779	93,855
1996	2,548,948	605,413	133,467	102,699
1997	2,541,910	657,562	159,215	115,738

*Excluding Cork University Hospital, for which figures on private days in public beds and vice versa were not available.

A substantial proportion of this "crossover", of private patients in public beds and vice versa, occurs in a small number of hospitals. Five hospitals accounted for almost half of the total private bed-days spent in designated public beds in 1997. These were University Hospital, Galway, Limerick Regional, and St. James', St. Vincent's and Beaumont Hospitals in Dublin. (The same hospitals also accounted for 34 per cent of the total bed-days spent by public patients in designated private beds.)

A similar analysis can be carried out for day beds used, on the basis of the figures reported to the Department via the monitoring system. Table 7.2 shows the public/private usage pattern for day beds in 1995, 1996 and 1997. We see that in

1997, 16 per cent of the day beds used by private patients were in designated public beds.

TABLE 7.2: PUBLIC VERSUS PRIVATE DAY BED USAGE IN PUBLIC HOSPITALS, 1995-1997

	Total Bed Days Used by Public Patients	Total Bed Days Used by Private Patients	Private Bed-Days in Public Beds	Public Bed-Days in Private Beds
1995	108,735	26,320	4,168	1,222
1996	127,992	30,198	4,086	756
1997	137,380	30,715	4,785	1,484

Both in the case of in-patient stays and day bed care, then, the current reporting system reveals a significant "crossover" of private patients receiving care in designated public beds and vice versa. The reasons why these crossovers take place were investigated in the course of this study by discussion with the Department of Health and Children and with hospital management and medical consultants. Public patients received care in private beds either simply due to unavailability of public beds, or because of the unavailability of suitable beds to meet the need for privacy for terminally ill patients or isolation for those with infectious diseases. The key factor identified by hospital management leading to private patients being accommodated in public beds was admission through accident/emergency departments of patients opting for private status (either then or subsequently) at a point when no private beds were available. A common reaction from hospital management and consultants was that this pointed to a growing mismatch between the number of private beds available and the numbers in the population now having private health insurance.

This obviously raises issues to which we return in our concluding chapter. At this point, however, our focus is on the specific issue of the bed designation arrangements and how they are operating and being monitored. The overall scale of the occupation of designated public beds by private patients must first be put in perspective. If public beds were entirely occupied by public patients, this would represent an increase of 6 per cent (in 1997) in the number of hospital nights available to public patients, assuming the existing level of "reverse cross-over" — public patients spending time in designated private beds — continued. If public patients were entirely and exclusively accommodated in public beds, on the other hand — there was no crossover — that would represent an increase of only 1.7 per cent in total public bed-nights.

Consultations with the Department of Health and Children and hospital management do not suggest that elective admissions of private patients to public beds are taking place. It is worth noting however that the present monitoring system does not provide for hospital management to validate for the Department that all admissions of private patients to public beds are taking place through accident and emergency departments. Secondly, the arrangements initially set out that a private patient may occupy a public bed provided that the consultant certifies that an emergency admission is required, with similar certification where a public patient is admitted to a private bed through emergency. We were unable to establish whether such certification takes place in each hospital, and there is certainly no attempt to collate and report it centrally as part of the monitoring system.

We have seen that the incidence of "crossover" is quite concentrated in a small number of hospitals. It may be that efforts to improve reporting and monitoring of the arrangements could best be piloted with those hospitals, before assessing their effectiveness and whether they should be extended to all hospitals. It is also worth noting in this context the point made in Chapter 3 about recent changes to the information obtained by HIPE. Information on the public/private status of the patient is now being reported, but the public/private status of the bed they occupy is not: this means that the improved data in HIPE will have little direct benefit in terms of monitoring the arrangements.

The final point to be made with respect to the bed designation arrangements is that there are other means of influencing behaviour in this regard, beyond the framing, implementing and monitoring of the arrangements themselves. The Revised Contract for Consultant Medical Staff, applicable since 1998, provides for agreement regarding public versus private workloads, recognising equity of access as a critical principle, to be specified in Service Plans. This clearly has the potential to be a key policy instrument in relation to equity of access. More broadly, the economic incentives facing those hospital management and individual consultants need to be carefully assessed in terms of their likely impact on the balance between public and private care — a point to which we also return in our concluding chapter.

7.3 Equity of Access and Waiting Times

Waiting times for public versus private patients are of central concern in the context of equity of access. Data on waiting lists for public patients is gathered by the Department, covering the length of time such patients wait for certain procedures from time of diagnosis. Data produced in response to Parliamentary Questions in the Dail show that the total number of patients on public waiting lists for specified procedures was almost 34,000 at end-March 1998. Details of the breakdown of such totals by the nature of the treatment or specialty and by hospital have also been produced. Of this 1998 total, for example, 7,500 cases were waiting for ear, nose and throat treatment, over 6,000 for orthopaedic care, and about 3,000 for each of oncology, surgery, and gynaecology. The Mater and Beaumont Hospitals in Dublin and University Hospital, Galway were the hospitals with the largest waiting lists at that date, with 2,500-3,000 patients each.

The problems in interpreting trends over time in waiting lists have been amply rehearsed elsewhere, but they do clearly provide essential information to any assessment of ease of access to public hospital care for public patients. The length of waiting lists have been of major concern to policy-makers, and each year since 1993 Waiting List Initiatives have been allocated special budgets targeted at reducing the numbers on these lists. The stated aim of this Initiative at present is to reduce waiting times for in-patient procedures in public hospitals to no longer than 12 months for adults and six months for children in target specialties. A Review Group has reported on the efficacy of these measures (1998), and it is not our aim in this study to go over this ground. The length of time people have to wait for public hospital care as a public versus a private patient is, however, a crucial aspect of equity of access, and we have seen in previous chapters that perceptions about this aspect of the public system can play a key role in forming attitudes to private health care and insurance. We thus felt it was important in the course of this study to form a picture of the information currently available in respect of waiting times and to pinpoint gaps in that information.

The waiting time data for public patients currently gathered by hospitals and reported to the Department of Health and Children refer to the time from point of diagnosis, at which point the patient goes on the waiting list for a particular type of care. This means that time spent waiting for a consultation in the first place, which could differ greatly for public and private patients, is not taken into account. In addition, to capture the position of public versus private patients one would like to compare waiting times for public and private patients, and the implicit assumption that private patients do not have to wait may not be valid now, even if it was at some earlier date. (The attitudinal survey results reported in Chapter 6, for example, did suggest some private patients had significant waiting times). However, no data on private patient waiting times is available from official sources.

In seeking additional data on utilisation and costs from selected public hospitals as described in Chapters 3 and 4, reflecting these concerns we also sought information on waiting times. We asked hospitals for a description of any data gathered in the hospital records on length of time from referral to first specialist consultation and then from consultation/diagnosis to receipt of treatment, and also whether any information was gathered on waiting times for private patients. A small number of responding hospitals did have data on length of time spent between referral and first specialist consultation, showing that in some instances considerable periods were involved. Virtually no information was available to hospitals on waiting times for private patients, this being generally regarded as a matter for the individual consultant.

7.4 Conclusions

In this chapter we have focused primarily on the new arrangements for access to care for public versus private patients in public hospitals introduced in the early 1990s. Under these arrangements most beds in public hospitals have been designated as for public or private use, and the extent to which private patients are accommodated in public beds and vice versa is monitored. Under the arrangements, private patients are defined as those opting to avail of private consultant services, rather than simply someone who has private health insurance cover. We saw that about 24 per cent of all in-patient bed-days spent by private patients in public hospitals were in beds designated as public. A smaller but still substantial absolute number of bed-days was spent by public patients in designated private beds. A substantial proportion of this "crossover" occurs in a small number of hospitals, with five hospitals accounting for about half the total private bed-days spent in designated public beds. As far as day-cases are concerned, 16 per cent of all the day-beds used by private patients were in designated public beds.

The reasons why these crossovers take place were investigated in the course of this study by discussion with the Department of Health and Children and with hospital management and medical consultants. Public patients received care in private beds either simply due to unavailability of public beds, or because of the unavailability of suitable beds to meet the need for privacy for terminally ill patients or isolation for those with infectious diseases. The key factor identified by hospital management leading to private patients being accommodated in public beds was admission through accident/emergency departments of patients opting for private status (either then or subsequently) at a point when no private beds were available. If public beds were entirely occupied by public patients, the number of hospital nights available to public patients would be increased by 6 per cent (in 1997), assuming public patients continued to be accommodated in designated private beds. If public patients were entirely and exclusively accommodated in public beds, on the other hand, that would represent an increase of less than 2 per cent in total public bed-nights.

While there is no evidence to suggest that elective admissions of private patients to public beds are taking place, the present monitoring system does not provide for hospital management to validate that all admissions of private patients to public beds are taking place through accident and emergency departments. Consultant certification that an emergency admission is required in such cases, originally envisaged in the arrangements, is not built into the monitoring system. Efforts to improve reporting and monitoring of the arrangements could be piloted in those hospitals where "crossover" is most prevalent, before assessing their effectiveness and whether they should be extended to all hospitals. Other means of influencing behaviour in this regard are also available, including the way contracts with consultant medical staff are monitored and the way economic incentives facing hospital management and individual consultants are structured.

Waiting times for public versus private patients are clearly of central concern in the context of equity of access. Data on waiting lists for public patients is gathered by the Department of Health and Children, covering the length of time such patients wait for certain procedures from time of diagnosis. Additional data available to hospitals on waiting times were explored in the course of this study. A small number of responding hospitals did have data on length of time spent between referral and first specialist consultation, showing that in some instances considerable periods were involved. Virtually no information was available to hospitals on waiting times for private patients, this being generally regarded as a matter for the individual consultant.

Chapter 8

Key Findings and Implications

8.1 Introduction

Previous chapters have presented the results of various analyses carried out in the course of the study, to provide a basis for consideration of the key policy issues identified in our terms of reference. In this concluding chapter we first bring together and summarise these key findings, in Section 8.2. In Section 8.3 we then draw on these to consider the likely impact of moving towards charging private patients in public hospitals the cost of provision of care, and the implications for policy aimed at meeting the principles of the health strategy in relation to equity, quality and accountability.

8.2 Key Findings

We began our analysis of private practice in public hospitals by focusing first on the stock of public versus private beds. Since the early 1990s, most beds in acute public hospitals are designated as for either public or private use. About 20 per cent of in-patient beds in acute public hospitals are currently designated as being for private patient use, while about 32 per cent of day beds are so designated. Turning to patients rather than beds, a private patient in a public hospital is someone opting to avail of private consultant services, rather than simply someone who has private health insurance. The proportion of all bed-days spent in public hospitals accounted for by private patients rose from 18 per cent in 1995 to 21 per cent in 1997, with private patients accounting for about the same proportion of day bed use.

We then sought to look in more detail at the private and public workload in public hospitals, in particular the characteristics of the case-mix involved. We had to rely however on data reported in the Hospital In-Patient Inquiry which (then) distinguished only GMS from non-GMS patients. About two-thirds of those not covered by a medical card have private health insurance. The differences in the extent and nature of utilisation of public hospital care between those with and without medical card cover are not only very interesting in their own right, they also provide an indication of the differences between public and private patients.

This analysis of acute inpatients revealed important differences in bed-day consumption and case mix intensity between GMS and non-GMS patients. In 1996 and 1997, GMS patients accounted for 44 per cent of the public hospital discharges reported through the HIPE. However, patients with medical card cover accounted for about 54 per cent of all bed-days and had an average length of stay about 25 per cent longer than non-GMS patients. This was clearly related to the differing age profiles of the two groups, with the average age of GMS patients being almost 50 compared with only 38 for other patients. This had major implications for both the nature of the conditions occurring in each group and the care provided. In particular, GMS patients were more likely to have been treated for a medical condition, and the non-GMS patients were more likely to have had a surgical procedure, when in hospital. Turning to case mix as measured by the Diagnosis Related Group classification system, over 40 per cent of GMS patients were in the Major Diagnostic Categories relating to the respiratory system, the circulatory system and the digestive system, which was a higher degree of concentration than for non-GMS patients. Within DRGs, GMS patients still tended to have longer average length of stay.

We then went on to explore the implications of these differences in the types of care provided to GMS and non-GMS patients for the resource use of these two groups, again serving as a proxy for differences between public and private patients. Non-GMS patients were found to be more costly per day spent in hospital. In terms of the costs taken into account in the Department of Health and Children's specialty costing exercise, the case-mix adjusted cost per day spent in hospital by a non-GMS patient in 1997 was estimated at £246, compared with £230 for GMS patients. This assumes that the average costs from the Department of Health's specialty costing estimates can reasonably be applied to both private and public patients. Efforts to obtain further relevant information from public hospitals on costing met with limited success, though this data-gathering exercise did however help to identify key gaps in the information regularly gathered for administrative and policy-making purposes. As well as relating to average costs, the costing information currently available is not comprehensive in that the specialty costing exercise does not seek to incorporate all costs — such as for example costs of training.

With the very limited information available, however, it is clear that the cost of provision of private care in public hospitals substantially exceeds the current level of charges for such care. Even given all the gaps in the information currently available, the cost of provision may be as much as twice the charge currently levied on a semi-private bed. With about one in five patients in public hospitals receiving private care, and that care more costly on a per-night basis than the care received by public patients, about one-quarter of the direct cost of providing in-patient care may be attributable to private patients. The direct costs of providing care, taken into account in the costing exercise, fall well short of total expenditure on acute hospitals. Concentrating on direct costs, however, these initial estimates suggested that private patients may have accounted for about £130 million in expenditure on direct provision of care in 1996. This amounted to about twice the income from charges for private accommodation in that year, with private patients also subsidised through tax relief on health insurance premia.

In the next two chapters we then sought to assess the implications of increased charges for private care in public hospitals for the demand for private insurance, the major mechanism through which the demand for private care itself would be affected. Time-series analysis of data on the evolution of health insurance in Ireland examined whether key influences — and particularly that of price — could be identified. The results were at best to be seen as suggestive, given unsatisfactory statistical aspects of the estimated equations and the fact that potentially important explanatory variables relating to perceptions of the public health service could not be included. Like similar studies elsewhere, they do suggest that a negative effect of price increases on the demand for insurance in Ireland can be detected over the whole period in which insurance has operated, serving to damp down what would otherwise have been an even more pronounced upward trend. Reductions in tax relief should have contributed to a greater negative price effect on the demand for health insurance over the past decade, but that was not evident in the results.

We then looked at what could be learned about the nature of demand for private health insurance in Ireland by in-depth examination of the characteristics of those who have insurance, making use of household survey data gathered by the ESRI in 1994. This showed, for example, that coverage was highest in the 35-54 age range, was higher for married than single adults, and was higher in Dublin than elsewhere. Coverage rose markedly with household income, but some of those covered were in the bottom half of the household income distribution, and a significant minority at the top did not have cover. Similarly coverage was highest for the professional/managerial social classes, but significant numbers in the manual social classes have cover. The proportion with cover was particularly high for the self-employed, while among employees those in clerical and professional occupations were most likely to have cover. These results highlight the extent to which health insurance cover has penetrated in recent years well beyond the upper reaches of the income distribution and social class hierarchy.

Econometric analysis of the way in which various characteristics of individuals and their households influence the demand for health insurance, carried out with Dr. Colm Harmon of UCD, showed that education level attained, household income, age and marital status were all significant predictors of that probability. Incorporating measures of self-reported health suggested that, controlling for other characteristics, poor health made one less rather than more likely to have insurance: there was no evidence of adverse selection, though one would ideally like more comprehensive measures of health.

The 1997 *Living in Ireland Survey*, which followed up those interviewed in 1994, revealed some movement in and out of insurance between those dates. About one-third of respondents were insured in both surveys, but 4 per cent of respondents were insured in 1994 but no longer insured by 1997, while 5.5 per cent were not insured in 1994 but had become insured by 1997. Those who remained insured were more heavily concentrated in the 35-54 age range, in the top half of the income distribution, in the professional/managerial social classes, and in owner-occupied housing than those moving in or out of insurance. An increase in the frequency of employer provision of health insurance as a benefit was also observed between the two surveys.

Results from an attitudinal survey carried out in 1999 also shed a good deal of light on why people buy health insurance. Almost all those who had insurance said being sure of getting into hospital was an important reason. However, being sure of getting good treatment, being sure of getting consultant care, and fear of large hospital bills were also very widely regarded as important. Compared with the pattern of responses from a similar exercise carried out in 1991, while access remained a key reason for having health insurance, issues relating to quality of care appeared to have become somewhat more important over the 1990s. Those with insurance appeared relatively insensitive to a price increase next year of the order of 10-20 per cent, though over one-third said they would be very likely to give up insurance if the price went up by 50 per cent.

Almost half the insured said they personally knew someone who had recently had a lengthy wait for public hospital treatment, and two-thirds believed that waiting times for treatment in public hospitals were longer now than five years ago. This was also true of those without health insurance, of whom about one-third said that if waiting times for public hospitals were to get longer in the future, that would make them much more likely to buy health insurance. About 3 per cent of respondents said they were currently on a waiting list for in-patient treatment: 20 per cent of these had been waiting for more than a year. While it was a good deal more common for those without insurance, some respondents with insurance were waiting for in-patient treatment.

The arrangements for access to care for public versus private patients in public hospitals introduced in the early 1990s, whereby most beds in public hospitals have been designated as for public or private use, were then considered. About 23 per cent of all in-patient bed-days spent by private patients in public hospitals were in beds designated as public. A slightly smaller absolute number of bed-days was spent by public patients in designated private beds. A substantial proportion of this "crossover" occurs in a small number of hospitals. About 15 per cent of all the day-beds used by private patients were in designated public beds.

The key factor identified by hospital management leading to private patients being accommodated in public beds was admission through accident/emergency departments of patients opting for private status (either then or subsequently) when no private beds were available. If public beds were entirely occupied by public patients, the number of hospital nights available to public patients would be increased by 6 per cent (in 1997), assuming public patients continued to be accommodated in designated private beds.

Waiting times for public versus private patients are clearly of central concern in the context of equity of access. Data on waiting lists for public patients for specified procedures are gathered by the Department of Health and Children; the availability of additional data to hospitals on waiting times was explored in the course of this study. Some hospitals did have data on length of time spent between referral and first specialist consultation, but virtually no information was available to hospitals on waiting times for private patients.

8.3 Implications of the Findings

A key issue for this study has been the likely effects of moving to charging the full cost of provision for private care in public hospitals. As we saw, analysis of HIPE data showed that the average cost of care per day for non-GMS in-patients in 1997 was

£246, compared with £230 for GMS patients. This figure has to be seen as a crude first estimate of the cost of care for private patients given all the gaps in information required to arrive at an adequate estimate. The fact that the public/private status of patients is now to be collected by the HIPE represents a significant enhancement in the database for analysis of the private workload in public hospitals. However, the results produced here provide a benchmark from which to assess the implications of the stated policy of moving towards charging full economic cost for private care in public hospitals.

We noted earlier that the concept of "full economic cost" is not unambiguous, and the appropriate basis for arriving at the charge one would actually wish to levy is not simply determined by a costing exercise. Rather than average cost, one might want to focus on all the *additional* costs associated with providing private care, taking into account not only the immediate direct costs, but also the longer-term impact of those higher activity levels on the hospital as a whole, including capital costs. In addition, decisions about charging for private care in public hospitals cannot but be influenced by the nature of the market for private care, the availability, costs and charging policy of private care in private hospitals, and the nature of the health insurance market and the approaches adopted by insurers. Suppose however that the level of charges for private care in public hospitals was doubled: what would be the impact on the demand for health insurance?

An increase of this order of magnitude would be likely — *ceteris paribus* — to increase annual claims facing insurers by one-quarter. If such an increase in charges was implemented all at once, and produced an immediate increase of that scale in the level of premia, it would clearly represent a substantial increase by historical standards, though not wholly unprecedented. The evidence from other countries, from our time-series analysis of Irish experience, and from attitudinal responses suggest that this would be sufficient to have a noticeable impact, reducing the numbers purchasing health insurance. However, a continuation of the policy of phased increases from year to year, moving towards the higher level of charges over a lengthy period of years, would have rather less impact.

One could for example envisage increased charges leading to an additional increase — over and above the rate of increase arising for other reasons — of under 5 per cent per year for five years. Recent experience suggests that the forces leading to increasing demand for health insurance in the Irish case are powerful. Both attitudinal responses and this recent experience suggest that annual increases in the cost of insurance in excess of those recently seen, while they might indeed be enough to cause the rate of increase in numbers insured to tail off for a time, would not be enough in themselves to produce a dramatic reduction in the numbers insured.

This is of course dependent on those forces promoting demand for insurance continuing to operate. Two key influences are likely to be economic growth and perceptions of the care available to public patients. Economic growth appears set to continue at a healthy, if somewhat slower, rate over the next decade: if it does not, and in particular if the level of investment and job creation by the multinational sector fell away sharply, then the implications of price increases for the demand for insurance could be very different. The prospects for perceptions of the care available to public patients are if anything even harder to assess. They will of course depend on the quality and availability of that care, and on indicators available to the public such as waiting lists.

Apart from the potential impact through the numbers with private health insurance, an increase in the cost of private care in public hospitals might, on the face of it, be expected to lead to a switch of private patients from public to private hospitals. This does not seem likely to be particularly pronounced given the present mode of operation by the dominant health insurer, where choice of hospital seems effectively to be at the discretion of the medical consultant. (Indeed, one might have expected a response by the insurer to the incentive to direct private patients to the much cheaper private care currently available in public hospitals.) If choices between hospitals are to be prompted by insurers on the basis of cost, then the relevant comparison clearly becomes the cost of private care in private versus public hospitals, and a significant increase in the latter would not serve to make them uncompetitive.

This comparison does point however to an important issue about charges in the context of such an increase. In terms of the incentive offered, it seems entirely unsatisfactory to have the charge levied simply on a per-night basis, irrespective of the nature and cost of the care provided to the individual patient. Moving towards a significantly higher average level of cost would seem to provide a suitable context in which to move away from such a flat charge across all patients, towards one which reflected the nature of the treatment provided. With private hospitals adopting a similar approach, one would then have a more economically rational pricing system facing the different actors in the market, notably insurers.

Equity in access by private versus public patients to public hospitals is intrinsically difficult to monitor, but the present monitoring system clearly has limitations. For example, it does not provide for hospital management to validate that all admissions of private patients to public beds are taking place through accident and emergency departments, or for consultant certification that an emergency admission is required in such cases. Improvements to the reporting and monitoring of the arrangements could be piloted in those hospitals where "crossover" is most prevalent, before assessing their effectiveness and whether they should be extended to all hospitals. The absence of any information on cost of private versus public patients within specialities is also a major limitation. Such a breakdown by public/private status for the specialty costing exercise could be introduced gradually, beginning with those cost centres where the public/private breakdown is most significant. Improving these monitoring systems would still leave the larger issue of the appropriate scale of private versus public care to be addressed. The stock of private beds in public hospitals is a key policy parameter. With the proportion of overnight beds designated as private held static over the past decade and the numbers covered by insurance growing rapidly, the pressure on these beds has clearly grown and increasing the price to full cost may not in itself suffice to bring supply and demand into balance.

Achieving that balance is not, however, the goal which the public/private mix is intended to promote. The primary aim of public policy in this regard, as we interpret the available strategy and policy statements, is to directly promote quality of care in public hospitals via the standard of expertise and facilities — rather than to, for example, raise additional revenue which could indirectly serve the same objective. In that light, the key criterion on which choices about the extent and nature of, and charges for, private care in public hospitals should be what the impact will be on public patients. Increasing the stock of private beds then seems likely to be counter-productive: instead, the focus of policy would be on ensuring that the presumed benefits to public patients of the existing public/private mix actually materialise.

Regulating the number of private beds in public hospitals, setting the relevant charges, and monitoring their use are important levers but not the only ones available to policy-makers. The economic incentives currently facing the different agents involved in private care in public hospitals could also be reoriented. Hospital consultants currently receive payment (from insurers) for treating patients in public hospitals who opt for private status, whether they are accommodated in public or private beds. The hospital, on the other hand, receives payment only where a private bed is occupied. Increasing levels of income over the anticipated level from delivering private care in private beds add to the resources available to the hospital in a given year, though over time there appears to be some clawback as public funding adjusts to the expected level of private revenue. The fully insured patient is financially unaffected by whether private care is received in a public or private hospital, and in the former by whether a public or private bed is occupied. The insurer pays most for care of its customers when that care is received in a private hospital, less than that when it is delivered in a private bed in a public hospital, and least when it is delivered in a public bed.

Changes in this complex structure of incentives could significantly alter the nature of the regulation required to promote equity of access. If, for example, consultants (as well as hospitals) were paid for private care only when that was delivered in a private hospital or a designated private bed in a public hospital, then there would be no direct incentive to maximise the number of private patients treated in designated public beds. If on the other hand hospitals (as well as consultants) were to be paid for care to patients opting for private status, whether treated in a designated private or public bed, the incentive to maximise the number of private patients treated in designated public beds would be significantly increased.

An emphasis on clear separation of public and private care within public hospitals and a desire to see such private care "pay its way" seem to represent the main features of the current policy stance. Of course, the current institutional structure is not cast in stone, and a range of more or less radical shifts in the balance of the public-private mix has been advocated. Before one can assess alternative strategies, however, once again a clear picture of the benefits and costs to public patients of the current public-private mix is essential. The present study has sought to provide some of the building blocks necessary to the pursuit of this objective, in terms of both concrete results and highlighting key gaps in the data available.

Appendix 1

List of Persons Consulted in the Course of the Study

Barton, Vincent; Cregan, Joseph; Flynn, Fergal; Hardy, Charles; Magee, Hugh; Harkin, Anna May; and Lynch, Fergal
Department of Health and Children

Brennan, Dr. Neil, Mercy Hospital Cork/IMO

Carr, Dr. Bernadette, VHI

Crowe, Dr. John, Mater Hospital

Crown, Dr. John, St. Vincent's Hospital

Fennell, Dr. William, Cork University Hospital

Fitzgerald, Professor Muiris, St. Vincent's Hospital

Fitzpatrick, Mr. Finbar, Independent Hospitals Association of Ireland

Heavey, Mr. Michael, Independent Hospitals Association of Ireland

Lynott, Ms. Maureen, BUPA Ireland

Lyons, Mr. Pat, CEO, Beaumont Hospital

Moran, Mr. Mark, CEO, Mater Private Hospital

O'Brien, Mr. John, CEO, St. James' Hospital

Appendix 2

DRG by Age Analysis by GMS Status in HIPE

A case mix analysis of GMS versus non-GMS patients at the DRG level was presented in Chapter 3, Tables 3.5a through 3.5d. The corresponding figures within the age ranges are given in this appendix, with Tables A1-A4 relating to the 0-14 age range, Tables B1-B4 to the 15-64 age range, and Tables C1-C4 for the 65 or over age range.

TABLE A1: TOP 30 DRGS FOR GMS PATIENTS, AGED 0-14, 1996

DRG	Diagnosis Related Group	Total	%	LOS (Days)	Bed Days	RV96
184	Oesophagitis, gastroenteritis & miscellaneous digestive disorders age 0-17	4,887	14.19	3.16	15,427	0.4156
70	Otitis media & upper respiratory infection age 0-17	2,983	8.66	2.95	8,795	0.3929
98	Bronchitis & asthma age 0-17	2,935	8.52	3.44	10,109	0.4975
422	Viral illness & fever of unknown origin age 0-17	1,624	4.71	2.56	4,157	0.3985
60	Tonsillectomy &/or adenoidectomy only, age 0-17	1,289	3.74	2.40	3,087	0.5371
30	Traumatic stupor & coma, coma <1 hr age 0-17	1,185	3.44	1.68	1,991	0.2716
26	Seizure & headache age 0-17	1,058	3.07	2.79	2,950	0.5200
91	Simple pneumonia & pleurisy age 0-17	817	2.37	5.28	4,310	0.6741
62	Myringotomy w tube insertion age 0-17	762	2.21	1.85	1,408	0.6003
252	Fracture, sprain, strain & dislocation of forearm, hand, foot age 0-17	725	2.10	1.32	957	0.2485

DRG	Diagnosis Related Group	Total	%	LOS (Days)	Bed Days	RV96
167	Appendectomy w/o complicated principal diagnosis w/o cc	713	2.07	4.21	3,002	0.7168
322	Kidney & urinary tract infections age 0-17	640	1.86	4.03	2,580	0.5725
282	Trauma to the skin, subcutaneous tissue & breast age 0-17	589	1.71	1.66	975	0.2813
102	Other respiratory system diagnoses w/o cc	543	1.58	3.67	1,990	0.5845
451	Poisoning & toxic effects of drugs age 0-17	520	1.51	1.70	884	0.3099
298	Nutritional & miscellaneous metabolic disorders age 0-17	492	1.43	6.83	3,359	0.8978
284	Minor skin disorders w/o cc	400	1.16	3.46	1,383	0.3814
41	Extraocular procedures except orbit age 0-17	397	1.15	1.99	790	0.5577
190	Other digestive system diagnoses age 0-17	391	1.14	2.64	1,033	0.5050
186	Dental & oral disorders except extractions & restorations, age 0-17	374	1.09	2.16	808	0.4663
467	Other factors influencing health status	353	1.03	2.81	991	0.5711
340	Testes procedures, non-malignancy age 0-17	331	0.96	1.97	653	0.6000
255	Fracture, sprain, strain & dislocation of upper arm, lower leg ex foot age 0-17	329	0.96	2.01	661	0.2986
279	Cellulitis age 0-17	320	0.93	4.02	1,285	0.4927
247	Signs & symptoms of musculoskeletal and connective tissue	285	0.83	3.15	898	0.4922
71	Laryngotracheitis	264	0.77	1.83	484	0.2327
55	Miscellaneous ear, nose, mouth & throat procedures	257	0.75	2.36	607	0.8391
74	Other ear, nose, mouth & throat diagnoses age 0-17	253	0.73	2.04	516	0.3667
343	Circumcision age 0-17	249	0.72	1.55	386	0.5028
256	Other musculoskeletal system & connective tissue diagnoses	216	0.63	3.62	782	0.6022
		26,181	75.99	2.95	77,258	

In-patients with LOS 0-30 days

TABLE A2: TOP 30 DRGs FOR NON-GMS PATIENTS, AGED 0-14, 1996

DRG	Diagnosis Related Group	Total	%	LOS (Days)	Bed Days	RV96
184	Oesophagitis, gastroenteritis & miscellaneous digestive disorders age 0-17	6,341	12.77	2.62	16,593	0.4156
98	Bronchitis & asthma age 0-17	3,971	7.99	2.81	11,164	0.4975
70	Otitis media & uri age 0-17	3,557	7.16	2.36	8,410	0.3929
422	Viral illness & fever of unknown origin age 0-17	2,425	4.88	2.22	5,392	0.3985
60	Tonsillectomy &/or adenoidectomy only, age 0-17	2,015	4.06	2.31	4,660	0.5371
30	Traumatic stupor & coma, coma <1 hr age 0-17	1,828	3.68	1.49	2,721	0.2716
252	Fracture, sprain, strain & dislocation of forearm, hand, foot age 0-17	1,512	3.04	1.23	1,855	0.2485
26	Seizure & headache age 0-17	1,336	2.69	2.66	3,557	0.5200
167	Appendectomy w/o complicated principal diagnosis w/o cc	1,214	2.44	4.07	4,944	0.7168
91	Simple pneumonia & pleurisy age 0-17	1,137	2.29	4.31	4,903	0.6741
62	Myringotomy w tube insertion age 0-17	1,128	2.27	1.93	2,173	0.6003
282	Trauma to the skin, subcutaneous tissue & breast age 0-17	956	1.93	1.49	1,423	0.2813
322	Kidney & urinary tract infections age 0-17	870	1.75	3.76	3,267	0.5725
451	Poisoning & toxic effects of drugs age 0-17	816	1.64	1.52	1,241	0.3099
389	Full term neonate with major problems	678	1.37	5.28	3,577	0.8596
255	Fracture, sprain, strain & dislocation of upper arm, lower leg ex foot age 0-17	635	1.28	1.79	1,134	0.2986
102	Other respiratory system diagnoses w/o cc	613	1.23	2.99	1,832	0.5845
467	Other factors influencing health status	610	1.23	2.39	1,455	0.5711

DRG	Diagnosis Related Group	Total	%	LOS (Days)	Bed Days	RV96
71	Laryngotracheitis	534	1.08	1.68	896	0.2327
190	Other digestive system diagnoses age 0-17	516	1.04	2.41	1,243	0.5050
284	Minor skin disorders w/o cc	514	1.04	2.89	1,484	0.3814
340	Testes procedures, non-malignancy age 0-17	482	0.97	1.85	891	0.6000
186	Dental & oral disorders except extractions & restorations age 0-17	473	0.95	1.84	870	0.4663
41	Extraocular procedures except orbit age 0-17	471	0.95	1.92	902	0.5577
390	Neonate with other significant problems	453	0.91	4.96	2,246	0.6447
298	Nutritional & miscellaneous metabolic disorders age 0-17	426	0.86	5.76	2,454	0.8978
247	Signs & symptoms of musculoskeletal and connective tissue	405	0.82	3.05	1,234	0.4922
270	Other skin, subcutaneous tissue & breast procedures w/o cc	350	0.71	1.49	521	0.6726
343	Circumcision age 0-17	349	0.70	1.47	514	0.5028
279	Cellulitis age 0-17	346	0.70	3.27	1,132	0.4927
		36,961	74.41	2.56	94,688	

In-patients with LOS 0-30 days

TABLE A3: TOP 30 DRGs FOR GMS PATIENTS, AGED 0-14, 1997

DRG	Diagnosis Related Group	Total	%	LOS (days)	Bed Days	RV97
184	Oesophagitis, gastroenteritis & miscellaneous digestive disorders age 0-17	4,676	14.39	3.14	14,663	0.4210
98	Bronchitis & asthma age 0-17	2,865	8.82	3.63	10,410	0.4975
70	Otitis media & uri age 0-17	2,625	8.08	2.90	7,602	0.4059
422	Viral illness & fever of unknown origin age 0-17	1,416	4.36	2.48	3,508	0.4244
60	Tonsillectomy &/or adenoidectomy only, age 0-17	1,161	3.57	2.42	2,807	0.5480
30	Traumatic stupor & coma, coma <1 hr age 0-17	1,107	3.41	1.71	1,895	0.2833
26	Seizure & headache age 0-17	980	3.02	2.95	2,891	0.5335
91	Simple pneumonia & pleurisy age 0-17	771	2.37	4.91	3,784	0.6981
252	Fracture, sprain, strain and dislocation of forearm, hand, foot age 0-17	761	2.34	1.23	934	0.2445
167	Appendectomy w/o complicated principal diagnosis w/o cc	704	2.17	4.23	2,978	0.7077
62	Myringotomy w tube insertion age 0-17	620	1.91	1.88	1,164	0.6082
322	Kidney & urinary tract infections age 0-17	609	1.87	4.03	2,453	0.5872
451	Poisoning & toxic effects of drugs age 0-17	603	1.86	1.51	910	0.3089
282	Trauma to the skin, subcut tiss & breast age 0-17	594	1.83	1.66	988	0.2755
102	Other respiratory system diagnoses w/o cc	496	1.53	3.35	1,663	0.5850
284	Minor skin disorders w/o cc	450	1.39	3.12	1,403	0.3909
298	Nutritional & miscellanous metabolic disorders age 0-17	449	1.38	6.07	2,723	0.6839
467	Other factors influencing health status	411	1.27	2.86	1,174	0.5074
190	Other digestive system diagnoses age 0-17	402	1.24	2.54	1,022	0.4811
255	Fracture, sprain, strain and dislocation of upper arm, lower leg ex foot age 0-17	336	1.03	1.81	608	0.2943

DRG	Diagnosis Related Group	Total	%	LOS (days)	Bed Days	RV97
41	Extraocular procedures except orbit age 0-17	311	0.96	2.02	627	0.5656
186	Dental & oral dis except extractions & restorations age 0-17	302	0.93	2.21	668	0.5147
340	Testes procedures, non-malignancy age 0-17	297	0.91	1.84	547	0.6035
279	Cellulitis age 0-17	287	0.88	3.83	1,098	0.4901
247	Signs & symptoms of musculoskeletal and connective tissue	267	0.82	2.55	681	0.5028
74	Other ear, nose, mouth & throat diagnoses age 0-17	224	0.69	2.20	492	0.3874
71	Laryngotracheitis	219	0.67	1.87	410	0.2115
100	Respiratory signs & symptoms w/o cc	209	0.64	3.14	657	0.4184
270	Other skin, subcut tissue & breast w/o cc	208	0.64	1.77	369	0.6836
256	Other musculoskeletal system & connective tissue diagnoses	200	0.62	2.65	529	0.5953
		24,560	75.59	2.92	71,658	

In-patients with LOS 0-30 days

TABLE A4: TOP 30 DRGS FOR NON-GMS PATIENTS, AGED 0-14, 1997

DRG	Diagnosis Related Group	Total	%	LOS (Days)	Bed Days	RV97
184	Oesophagitis, gastroenteritis & miscellaneous digestive disorders age 0-17	6,368	13.31	2.66	16,959	0.4210
98	Bronchitis & asthma age 0-17	3,814	7.97	2.85	10,862	0.4975
70	Otitis media & uri age 0-17	3,193	6.68	2.31	7,383	0.4059
422	Viral illness & fever of unknown origin age 0-17	2,116	4.42	2.32	4,900	0.4244
60	Tonsillectomy &/or adenoidectomy only, age 0-17	1,837	3.84	2.35	4,312	0.5480
30	Traumatic stupor & coma, coma <1 hr age 0-17	1,758	3.68	1.55	2,719	0.2833
252	Fracture, sprain, strain & dislocation of forearm, hand, foot age 0-17	1,590	3.32	1.21	1,922	0.2445
91	Simple pneumonia & pleurisy age 0-17	1,344	2.81	4.30	5,775	0.6981
26	Seizure & headache age 0-17	1,278	2.67	2.69	3,432	0.5335
167	Appendectomy w/o complicated principal diagnosis w/o cc	1,222	2.56	4.10	5,004	0.7077
322	Kidney & urinary tract infections age 0-17	1,017	2.13	3.84	3,901	0.5872
282	Trauma to the skin, subcut tiss & breast age 0-17	960	2.01	1.51	1,445	0.2755
62	Myringotomy w tube insertion age 0-17	901	1.88	1.91	1,718	0.6082
451	Poisoning & toxic effects of drugs age 0-17	685	1.43	1.36	930	0.3089
255	Fracture, sprain, strain & dislocation of upper arm, lower leg ex foot age 0-17	647	1.35	1.91	1,238	0.2943
467	Other factors influencing health status	614	1.28	2.65	1,628	0.5074
389	Full term neonate w major problems	582	1.22	5.44	3,164	0.8681
102	Other respiratory system diagnoses w/o cc	548	1.15	2.95	1,616	0.5850
190	Other digestive system diagnoses age 0-17	544	1.14	2.44	1,329	0.4811

DRG	Diagnosis Related Group	Total	%	LOS (Days)	Bed Days	RV97
284	Minor skin disorders w/o cc	518	1.08	3.14	1,624	0.3909
186	Dental & oral dis except extractions & restoration age 0-17	508	1.06	2.11	1,070	0.5147
71	Laryngotracheitis	457	0.96	1.54	704	0.2115
340	Testes procedures, non-malignancy age 0-17	438	0.92	1.68	737	0.6035
385	Neonates, died or transferred to another acute care facility	437	0.91	4.47	1,953	1.8526
41	Extraocular procedures except orbit age 0-17	426	0.89	1.81	771	0.5656
247	Signs & symptoms of musculoskeletal and connective tissue	425	0.89	2.44	1,038	0.5028
298	Nutritional & misc metabolic disorders age 0-17	398	0.83	4.46	1,774	0.6839
390	Neonate with other significant problems	389	0.81	4.41	1,715	0.6175
279	Cellulitis age 0-17	383	0.80	3.47	1,328	0.4901
100	Respiratory signs & symptoms w/o cc	330	0.69	2.82	930	0.4184
		35,727	74.69	2.63	93,881	

In-patients with LOS 0-30 days

TABLE B1: TOP 30 DRGs FOR GMS PATIENTS AGED 15-64, 1996

DRG	Diagnosis Related Group	Total	%	LOS (Days)	Bed Days	RV96
183	Oesophagitis, gastroenteritis & miscellaneous digestive disorders age >17 w/o cc	4,661	5.42	3.56	16,601	0.4718
143	Chest pain	1,769	2.06	3.40	6,008	0.4449
450	Poisoning & toxic effects of drugs age >17 w/o cc	1,761	2.05	2.10	3,696	0.3386
25	Seizure & headache age >17 w/o cc	1,673	1.94	3.69	6,171	0.5789
88	Chronic obstructive pulmonary disease	1,404	1.63	7.54	10,580	1.0178
364	D&C conization except for malignancy	1,331	1.55	2.06	2,739	0.4958
243	Medical back problems	1,321	1.54	6.01	7,935	0.8090
140	Angina pectoris	1,310	1.52	6.08	7,960	0.8017
359	Uterine & adnexa proc for non-malignancy w/o cc	1,203	1.40	7.55	9,085	1.1657
410	Chemotherapy without acute leukemia as secondary diagnosis	1,078	1.25	2.59	2,792	0.7645
29	Traumatic stupor & coma, coma <1 hr age >17 w/o cc	1,056	1.23	2.10	2,220	0.3014
182	Oesophagitis, gastroenteritis & miscellaneous digestive disorders age >17 with cc	1,009	1.17	5.19	5,238	0.8378
119	Vein ligation & stripping	964	1.12	2.63	2,537	0.7191
97	Bronchitis & asthma age >17 w/o cc	951	1.11	4.52	4,301	0.5381
383	Other antepartum diagnoses with medical complications	925	1.08	2.83	2,621	0.0000
361	Laparoscopy & incisional tubal interruption	913	1.06	2.14	1,956	0.6022
167	Appendectomy w/o complicated principal diagnosis w/o cc	861	1.00	4.51	3,883	0.7168
69	Otitis media & uri age >17 w/o cc	726	0.84	3.20	2,321	0.4031
369	Menstrual & other female reproductive system disorders	721	0.84	2.64	1,903	0.3544
278	Cellulitis age >17 w/o cc	662	0.77	4.80	3,174	0.5646

DRG	Diagnosis Related Group	Total	%	LOS (Days)	Bed Days	RV96
449	Poisoning & toxic effects of drugs age >17 with cc	659	0.77	2.60	1,711	0.6157
381	Abortion with D&C, aspiration curettage or hysterotomy	652	0.76	2.18	1,420	0.0000
324	Urinary stones w/o cc	635	0.74	3.51	2,226	0.3915
184	Oesophagitis, gastroenteritis & miscellaneous digestive disorders age 0-17	624	0.73	2.93	1,830	0.4156
281	Trauma to the skin, subcut tiss & breast age >17 w/o cc	624	0.73	2.20	1,370	0.3349
208	Disorders of the biliary tract w/o cc	608	0.71	4.63	2,812	0.6907
321	Kidney & urinary tract infections age >17 w/o cc	590	0.69	3.95	2,332	0.5848
189	Other digestive system diagnoses age >17 w/o cc	585	0.68	3.04	1,777	0.4502
494	Laparoscopic cholecystectomy w/o C.D.E. w/o cc	568	0.66	4.84	2,751	0.9341
247	Signs & symptoms of musculoskeletal and connective tissue	565	0.66	3.90	2,203	0.4922
		32,409	37.67	3.83	124,153	

In-patients with LOS 0-30 days

TABLE B2: TOP 30 DRGs FOR NON-GMS PATIENTS, AGED 15-64, 1996

DRG	Diagnosis Related Group	Total	%	LOS (Days)	Bed Days	RV96
183	Oesophagitis, gastroenteritis & miscellaneous digestive disorders age >17 w/o cc	6,594	4.72	3.27	21,559	0.4718
373	Vaginal delivery w/o complicating diagnosis	4,006	2.87	4.14	16,595	0.0000
371	Cesarean section w/o cc	3,045	2.18	7.91	24,096	0.0000
381	Abortion w d&c, aspiration curettage or hysterotomy	2,816	2.02	1.73	4,877	0.0000
359	Uterine & adnexa proc for non-malignancy w/o cc	2,534	1.81	7.03	17,808	1.1657
383	Other antepartum diagnoses with medical complications	2,502	1.79	3.40	8,509	0.0000
29	Traumatic stupor & coma, coma <1 hr age >17 w/o cc	2,264	1.62	1.91	4,315	0.3014
143	Chest pain	2,256	1.61	3.26	7,355	0.4449
25	Seizure & headache age >17 w/o cc	2,168	1.55	3.57	7,744	0.5789
167	Appendectomy w/o complicated principal diagnosis w.o cc	2,132	1.53	4.30	9,173	0.7168
243	Medical back problems	2,086	1.49	6.27	13,075	0.8090
364	D&C, conization except for malignancy	1,772	1.27	1.86	3,292	0.4958
119	Vein ligation & stripping	1,702	1.22	2.39	4,074	0.7191
69	Otitis media & uri age >17 w/o cc	1,575	1.13	3.23	5,090	0.4031
450	Poisoning & toxic effects of drugs age >17 w/o cc	1,567	1.12	1.99	3,119	0.3386
361	Laparoscopy & incisional tubal interruption	1,509	1.08	2.11	3,185	0.6022
278	Cellulitis age >17 w/o cc	1,441	1.03	4.19	6,035	0.5646
219	Lower extrem & humer proc except hip, foot, femur age >17 w/o cc	1,435	1.03	6.19	8,880	1.1802
229	Hand or wrist proc, except major joint procedure, w/o cc	1,323	0.95	2.05	2,705	0.5901
324	Urinary stones w/o cc	1,286	0.92	3.00	3,851	0.3915
281	Trauma to the skin, subcut tiss & breast age >17 w/o cc	1,269	0.91	2.18	2,760	0.3349

Private Practice in Irish Public Hospitals

DRG	Diagnosis Related Group	Total	%	LOS (Days)	Bed Days	RV96
162	Inguinal & femoral hernia procedures age >17 w/o cc	1,265	0.91	3.10	3,927	0.7078
59	Tonsillectomy &/or adenoidectomy only, age > 17	1,259	0.90	3.21	4,039	0.5520
494	Laparoscopic cholecystectomy w/o C.D.E w/o cc	1,203	0.86	4.67	5,612	0.9341
379	Threatened abortion	1,198	0.86	2.59	3,104	0.0000
254	Fracture, sprain, strain & dislocation of upper arm, lower leg ex foot age > 17 w/o cc	1,155	0.83	2.75	3,178	0.3957
384	Other antepartum diagnoses w/o medical complications	1,147	0.82	3.24	3,712	0.0000
251	Fracture, sprain, strain & dislocation of forearm, hand, foot age > 17 w/o cc	1,108	0.79	1.87	2,074	0.3471
410	Chemotherapy without acute leukemia as secondary daignosis	1,099	0.79	2.49	2,738	0.7645
139	Cardiac arrhythmia & conduction discorders w/o cc	1,065	0.76	3.54	3,770	0.5675
		57,781	41.35	3.64	210,251	

In-patients with LOS 0-30 days

TABLE B3: TOP 30 DRGs FOR GMS PATIENTS, AGED 15-64, 1997

DRG	Diagnosis Related Group	Total	%	LOS (Days)	Bed Days	RV97
183	Oesophagitis, gastroenteritis & miscellaneous digestive disorders age >17 w/o cc	4,553	4.923	3.479	15,840	0.4620
373	Vaginal delivery w/o complicating diagnosis	2,733	2.955	3.707	10,131	0.0000
143	Chest pain	1,900	2.055	3.419	6,497	0.4546
450	Poisoning & toxic effects of drugs age >17 w/o cc	1,712	1.851	2.006	3,434	0.3441
25	Seizure & headache age >17 w/o cc	1,660	1.795	3.620	6,010	0.5516
88	Chronic obstructive pulmonary disease	1,579	1.707	7.590	11,984	1.0141
383	Other antepartum diagnoses with medical complications	1,475	1.595	2.782	4,104	0.0000
140	Angina pectoris	1,274	1.378	5.690	7,249	0.7352
243	Medical back problems	1,274	1.378	5.782	7,366	0.7650
359	Uterine & adnexa proc for non-malignancy w/o cc	1,255	1.357	7.022	8,812	1.1261
364	D&C, conization except for malignancy	1,168	1.263	1.883	2,199	0.5010
182	Oesophagitis, gastroenteritis & miscellaneous digestive disorders age >17 with cc	1,057	1.143	5.220	5,518	0.8252
29	Traumatic stupor & coma, coma <1 hr age >17 w/o cc	1,055	1.141	2.072	2,186	0.3183
97	Bronchitis & asthma age >17 w/o cc	906	0.980	4.380	3,968	0.5151
167	Appendectomy w/o complicated principal diagnosis w/o cc	899	0.972	4.249	3,820	0.7077
361	Laparoscopy & incisional tubal interruption	833	0.901	2.221	1,850	0.6086
119	Vein ligation & stripping	827	0.894	2.429	2,009	0.7168
69	Otitis media & uri age >17 w/o cc	817	0.883	3.241	2,648	0.4239
410	Chemotherapy without acute leukemia as secondary diagnosis	784	0.848	2.879	2,257	0.7320
449	Poisoning & toxic effects of drugs age >17 with cc	759	0.821	2.823	2,143	0.5943

DRG	Diagnosis Related Group	Total	%	LOS (Days)	Bed Days	RV97
369	Menstrual & other female reproductive system disorders	743	0.803	2.549	1,894	0.3624
371	Cesarean section w/o cc	727	0.786	7.415	5,391	0.0000
381	Abortion w d&c, aspiration curettage or hysterotomy	680	0.735	1.976	1,344	0.0000
184	Oesophagitis, gastroenteritis & miscellaneous digestive disorders age 0-17	669	0.723	3.010	2,014	0.4210
278	Cellulitis age >17 w/o cc	649	0.702	4.656	3,022	0.5627
494	Laparoscopic cholecystectomy w/o cde w/o cc	646	0.699	4.693	3,032	0.9089
281	Trauma to the skin, subcut tiss & breast age >17 w/o cc	641	0.693	2.109	1,352	0.3273
254	Fracture, sprain, strain & dislocation of upper arm, lower leg ex foot age >17 w/o cc	622	0.673	2.799	1,741	0.4190
247	Signs & symptoms of musculoskeletal and connective tissue	616	0.666	3.705	2,282	0.5028
294	Diabetes age >35	614	0.664	6.425	3,945	0.8337
		35,127	37.984	3.873	136,042	

In-patients with LOS 0-30 days

TABLE B4: TOP 30 DRGs FOR NON-GMS PATIENTS, AGED 15-64, 1997

DRG	Diagnosis Related Group	Total	%	LOS (Days)	Bed Days	RV97
373	Vaginal delivery w/o complicating diagnosis	12,121	8.03	3.92	47,467	0.0000
183	Oesophagitis, gastroenteritis & miscellaneous digestive disorders age >17 w/o cc	6,740	4.46	3.19	21,482	0.4620
383	Other antepartum diagnoses with medical complications	3,779	2.50	3.15	11,908	0.0000
371	Caesarean section w/o cc	3,547	2.35	7.57	26,864	0.0000
381	Abortion w d&c, aspiration curettage or hysterotomy	2,830	1.87	1.71	4,852	0.0000
359	Uterine & adnexa procedure for non-malignancy w/o cc	2,653	1.76	6.68	17,715	1.1261
167	Appendectomy w/o complicated principal diagnosis w/o cc	2,227	1.47	4.14	9,221	0.7077
143	Chest pain	2,223	1.47	3.14	6,978	0.4546
29	Traumatic stupor & coma, coma <1 hr age >17 w/o cc	2,206	1.46	2.05	4,523	0.3183
243	Medical back problems	2,052	1.36	5.90	12,111	0.7650
25	Seizure & headache age >17 w/o cc	1,972	1.31	3.41	6,725	0.5516
384	Other antepartum diagnoses w/o medical complications	1,685	1.12	2.87	4,837	0.0000
379	Threatened abortion	1,645	1.09	2.15	3,539	0.0000
361	Laparoscopy & incisional tubal interruption	1,641	1.09	2.09	3,433	0.6086
119	Vein ligation & stripping	1,552	1.03	2.30	3,565	0.7168
450	Poisoning & toxic effects of drugs age >17 w/o cc	1,548	1.03	2.15	3,327	0.3441
364	D&C, conization except for malignancy	1,538	1.02	1.83	2,821	0.5010
69	Otitis media & upper respiratory infection age >17 w/o cc	1,516	1.00	3.28	4,968	0.4239
278	Cellulitis age >17 w/o cc	1,466	0.97	4.25	6,229	0.5627
219	Lower extremity & humerus procedures except hip, foot, femur age >17 w/o cc	1,438	0.95	5.61	8,069	1.1014
229	Hand or wrist procedure, except major joint procedure, w/o cc	1,369	0.91	1.93	2,645	0.5733

DRG	Diagnosis Related Group	Total	%	LOS (Days)	Bed Days	RV97
251	Fracture, sprain, strain & dislocation of forearm, hand, foot age >17 w/o cc	1,314	0.87	1.61	2,113	0.3088
324	Urinary stones w/o cc	1,282	0.85	2.80	3,588	0.3818
281	Trauma to the skin, subcutaneous tissues & breast age >17 w/o cc	1,277	0.85	2.07	2,637	0.3273
162	Inguinal & femoral hernia procedures age >17 w/o cc	1,255	0.83	2.97	3,722	0.6706
59	Tonsillectomy &/or adenoidectomy only, age >17	1,231	0.82	3.19	3,932	0.5639
254	Fracture, sprain, strain & dislocation of upper arm, lower leg ex foot age >17 w/o cc	1,191	0.79	2.47	2,942	0.4190
494	Laparoscopic cholecystectomy w/o C.D.E. w/o cc	1,092	0.72	4.58	5,002	0.9089
369	Menstrual & other female reproductive system disorders	1,043	0.69	2.29	2,392	0.3624
139	Cardiac arrhythmia & conduction disorders w/o cc	1,035	0.69	3.52	3,642	0.5751
		68,468	45.33	3.55	243,249	

In-patients with LOS 0-30 days

TABLE C1: TOP 30 DRGS FOR GMS PATIENTS, AGED 65+, 1996

DRG	Diagnosis Related Group	Total	%	LOS (Days)	Bed Days	RV96
88	Chronic obstructive pulmonary disease	5,132	5.76	8.53	43,773	1.0178
183	Oesophagitis, gastroenteritis & miscellaneous digestive disorders age >17 w/o cc	3,910	4.39	5.60	21,885	0.4718
39	Lens procedures with or without vitrectomy	3,417	3.83	3.45	11,782	0.7312
127	Heart failure & shock	3,212	3.60	8.99	28,875	1.2575
89	Simple pneumonia & pleurisy age >17 with cc	2,266	2.54	9.68	21,936	1.3107
140	Angina pectoris	2,180	2.45	6.76	14,738	0.8017
14	Specific cerebrovascular disorders except transient ischaemic attack	2,126	2.39	11.16	23,725	1.9524
209	Major joint & limb reattachment procedures of lower extremity	2,026	2.27	16.05	32,524	3.3112
182	Oesophagitis, gastroenteritis & miscellaneous digestive disorders age >17 with cc	1,818	2.04	7.65	13,911	0.8378
395	Red blood cell disorders age >17	1,373	1.54	6.98	9,589	1.0509
101	Other respiratory system diagnoses with cc	1,358	1.52	8.71	11,833	1.0653
15	Transient ischemic attack & precerebral occlusions	1,267	1.42	7.32	9,268	0.8656
139	Cardiac arrhythmia & conduction disorders w/o cc	1,052	1.18	6.15	6,470	0.5675
143	Chest pain	1,026	1.15	4.76	4,881	0.4449
82	Respiratory neoplasms	1,015	1.14	9.47	9,607	1.4863
138	Cardiac arrhythmia & conduction disorders with cc	1,004	1.13	7.85	7,880	0.9694
102	Other respiratory system diagnoses w/o cc	961	1.08	7.69	7,392	0.5845
90	Simple pneumonia & pleurisy age >17 w/o cc	931	1.04	8.75	8,142	0.8191

DRG	Diagnosis Related Group	Total	%	LOS (Days)	Bed Days	RV96
122	Circulatory disorders with AMI w/o cardiovascular complication discharged alive	872	0.98	9.65	8,413	1.4628
131	Peripheral vascular disorders w/o cc	789	0.89	7.12	5,617	0.8084
294	Diabetes age >35	770	0.86	7.78	5,992	0.8586
208	Disorders of the biliary tract w/o cc	727	0.82	6.56	4,769	0.6907
132	Atherosclerosis with cc	708	0.79	7.30	5,165	1.0723
337	Transurethral prostatectomy w/o cc	705	0.79	7.62	5,373	0.9852
321	Kidney & urinary tract infections age > 17 w/o cc	704	0.79	7.21	5,074	0.5848
245	Bone diseases & specific arthropathies w/o cc	675	0.76	5.18	3,499	0.7500
130	Peripheral vascular disorders with cc	673	0.76	8.73	5,878	1.3147
236	Fractures of hip & pelvis	668	0.75	7.08	4,727	1.2766
243	Medical back problems	644	0.72	8.49	5,468	0.8090
467	Other factors influencing health status	629	0.71	8.54	5,372	0.5711
		44,638	50.07	7.92	353,558	

In-patients with LOS 0-30 days

TABLE C2: TOP 30 DRGs FOR NON-GMS PATIENTS, AGED 65+, 1996

DRG	Diagnosis Related Group	Total	%	LOS (Days)	Bed Days	RV97
183	Oesophagitis, gastroenteritis & miscellaneous digestive disorders age >17 w/o cc	1,387	3.62	5.51	7,643	0.4718
88	Chronic obstructive pulmonary disease	1,300	3.40	9.14	11,882	1.0178
127	Heart failure & shock	1,108	2.89	9.60	10,632	1.2575
39	Lens procedures with or without vitrectomy	1,058	2.76	2.96	3,135	0.7312
209	Major joint & limb reattachment procedures of lower extremity	1,042	2.72	15.45	16,101	3.3112
14	Specific cerebrovascular disorders except transient ischaemic attack	1,015	2.65	11.11	11,274	1.9524
140	Angina pectoris	809	2.11	6.74	5,450	0.8017
89	Simple pneumonia & pleurisy age >17 with cc	796	2.08	9.79	7,790	1.3107
182	Oesophagitis, gastroenteritis & miscellaneous digestive disorders age >17 with cc	610	1.59	7.90	4,820	0.8378
139	Cardiac arrhythmia & conduction discorders w/o cc	560	1.46	5.83	3,267	0.5675
15	Transient ischemic attack & precerebral occlusions	559	1.46	7.15	3,995	0.8656
122	Circulatory disorders with AMI w/o cardiovascular complication discharged alive	532	1.39	9.86	5,244	1.4628
337	Transurethral prostatectomy w/o cc	530	1.38	7.56	4,009	0.9852
138	Cardiac arrhythmia & conduction discorders w cc	457	1.19	8.51	3,891	0.9694
395	Red blood cell disorders age >17	402	1.05	8.15	3,278	1.0509
143	Chest pain	389	1.02	4.40	1,712	0.4449
101	Other respiratory system diagnoses with cc	388	1.01	9.06	3,516	1.0653
162	Inguinal & femoral hernia procedures age>17 w/o cc	381	1.00	4.82	1,836	0.7078
211	Hip & femur procedures except major age > 17 w/o cc	378	0.99	13.63	5,152	2.0541

DRG	Diagnosis Related Group	Total	%	LOS (Days)	Bed Days	RV97
82	Respiratory neoplasms	375	0.98	10.34	3,879	1.4863
90	Simple pneumonia & pleurisy age >17 w/o	354	0.93	8.99	3,181	0.8191
236	Fractures of hip & pelvis	343	0.90	7.84	2,689	1.2766
410	Chemotherapy without acute leukemia as secondary diagnosis	338	0.88	2.17	732	0.7645
132	Atherosclerosis with cc	322	0.84	8.13	2,617	1.0723
243	Medical back problems	313	0.82	7.94	2,486	0.8090
131	Peripheral vascular disorders w/o cc	307	0.80	6.20	1,903	0.8084
208	Disorders of the biliary tract w/o cc	306	0.80	5.94	1,817	0.6907
134	Hypertension	288	0.75	5.69	1,638	0.6585
121	Circulatory disorders w AMI & cardiovascular complication discharges alive	286	0.75	12.17	3,480	1.8529
294	Diabetes age >35	284	0.74	7.56	2,146	0.8586
		17,217	44.97	8.20	141,195	

In-patients with LOS 0-30 days

TABLE C3: TOP 30 DRGs FOR GMS PATIENTS, AGED 65+, 1997

DRG	Diagnosis Related Group	Total	%	LOS (Days)	Bed Days	RV97
88	Chronic obstructive pulmonary disease	5,437	6.00	8.46	45,973	1.0141
183	Oesophagitis, gastroenteritis & miscellaneous digestive disorders age >17 w/o cc	3,525	3.89	5.60	19,750	0.4620
127	Heart failure & shock	3,199	3.53	9.07	29,015	1.2828
39	Lens procedures with or without vitrectomy	3,148	3.47	3.32	10,456	0.7247
89	Simple pneumonia & pleurisy age >17 with cc	2,475	2.73	9.74	24,099	1.3071
182	Oesophagitis, gastroenteritis & miscellaneous digestive disorders age >17 with cc	2,099	2.31	7.37	15,461	0.8252
14	Specific cerebrovascular disorders except transient ischaemic attack	2,051	2.26	10.70	21,939	1.9779
209	Major joint & limb reattachment procedures of lower extremity	2,037	2.25	15.61	31,789	3.1460
140	Angina pectoris	2,006	2.21	6.63	13,296	0.7352
15	Transient ischemic attack & precerebral occlusions	1,431	1.58	7.11	10,171	0.8664
101	Other respiratory system diagnoses with cc	1,415	1.56	7.95	11,248	1.0344
395	Red blood cell disorders age >17	1,345	1.48	7.00	9,410	1.0363
138	Cardiac arrhythmia & conduction disorders with cc	1,196	1.32	8.26	9,879	1.0349
139	Cardiac arrhythmia & conduction disorder w/o cc	1,064	1.17	6.08	6,469	0.5751
143	Chest pain	1,021	1.13	4.93	5,028	0.4546
122	Circulatory disorders with AMI w/o cardiovascular complication discharged alive	968	1.07	9.52	9,219	1.4488
102	Other respiratory system diagnoses w/o cc	940	1.04	6.82	6,406	0.5850
82	Respiratory neoplasms	932	1.03	9.95	9,277	1.4282
90	Simple pneumonia & pleurisy age >17 w/o cc	851	0.94	8.32	7,084	0.7802
132	Atherosclerosis with cc	839	0.93	8.28	6,946	1.1413

DRG	Diagnosis Related Group	Total	%	LOS (Days)	Bed Days	RV97
294	Diabetes age >35	825	0.91	7.70	6,351	0.8337
131	Peripheral vascular disorders w/o cc	809	0.89	6.67	5,393	0.7824
208	Disorders of the biliary tract w/o cc	763	0.84	6.29	4,802	0.6886
130	Peripheral vascular disorders with cc	750	0.83	8.45	6,339	1.2321
321	Kidney & urinary tract infections age >17 w/o cc	742	0.82	7.12	5,283	0.6047
236	Fractures of hip & pelvis	709	0.78	7.63	5,409	1.4695
87	Pulmonary oedema & respiratory failure	668	0.74	9.40	6,278	1.3413
121	Circulatory disorders with AMI & cardiovascular complication discharged alive	624	0.69	11.14	6,951	1.9151
172	Digestive malignancy with cc	609	0.67	9.53	5,801	1.6594
245	Bone diseases & specific arthropathies w/o cc	608	0.67	4.79	2,912	0.6217
		45,086	49.71	7.95	358,434	

TABLE C4: TOP 30 DRGs FOR NON-GMS PATIENTS, AGED 65-120, 1997

DRG	Diagnosis Related Group	Total	%	LOS	Bed Days	RV97
183	Oesophagitis, gastroent & misc digest	1,224	3.29	5.46	6,688	0.4620
88	Chronic obstructive pulmonary disease	1,148	3.09	8.86	10,176	1.0141
209	Major joint & limb reattachment	1,059	2.85	15.13	16,024	3.1460
127	Heart failure & shock	1,054	2.83	9.70	10,224	1.2828
39	Lens procedures with or without	1,020	2.74	2.80	2,859	0.7247
14	Specific cerebrovascular disorders	1,004	2.70	11.02	11,060	1.9779
89	Simple pneumonia & pleurisy age >17 with	753	2.02	9.93	7,479	1.3071
140	Angina pectoris	710	1.91	6.58	4,671	0.7352
15	Transient ischemic attack & precerebral	620	1.67	7.21	4,467	0.8664
182	Oesophagitis, gastroent & misc digest	582	1.56	7.70	4,480	0.8252
139	Cardiac arrhythmia & conduction	562	1.51	5.54	3,113	0.5751
122	Circulatory disorders w ami w/o c.v.	543	1.46	9.52	5,171	1.4488
138	Cardiac arrhythmia & conduction	478	1.29	7.68	3,671	1.0349
337	Transurethral prostatectomy w/o cc	477	1.28	6.95	3,314	0.9432
395	Red blood cell disorders age >17	417	1.12	7.28	3,034	1.0363
143	Chest pain	416	1.12	4.43	1,844	0.4546
132	Atherosclerosis with cc	397	1.07	8.06	3,201	1.1413
101	Other respiratory system diagnoses with	353	0.95	8.35	2,946	1.0344
82	Respiratory neoplasms	351	0.94	9.09	3,192	1.4282
294	Diabetes age >35	341	0.92	7.56	2,577	0.8337
121	Circulatory disorders w ami & c.v. comp	339	0.91	11.57	3,921	1.9151
162	Inguinal & femoral hernia procedures age	334	0.90	4.40	1,469	0.6706

DRG	Diagnosis Related Group	Total	%	LOS	Bed Days	RV97
125	Circulatory disorders except ami, w card	328	0.88	5.65	1,852	0.8717
90	Simple pneumonia & pleurisy age >17 w/o	319	0.86	.36	2,668	0.7802
236	Fractures of hip & pelvis	307	0.83	7.95	2,440	1.4695
211	Hip & femur procedures except major	306	0.82	12.78	3,911	2.0037
208	Disorders of the biliary tract w/o cc	298	0.80	5.80	1,727	0.6886
410	Chemotherapy without acute leukemia as	282	0.76	2.39	674	0.7320
243	Medical back problems	278	0.75	8.34	2,318	0.7650
403	Lymphoma & non-acute leukemia w cc	278	0.75	8.40	2,334	1.9649
		16,578	44.56	8.05	133,505	

In-patients with LOS 0-30 days

References

Barrington, R. (1987). *Health, Medicine and Politics*, Dublin: IPA.

Besley, T., J. Hall and I. Preston (1998). "Private and Public Health Insurance in the UK", *European Economic Review*, Vol. 42, 491-497.

Besley, T., J. Hall and I. Preston (1999). "The Demand for Private Health Insurance: Do Waiting Lists Matter?", *Journal of Public Economics*, vol. 72 (2), 155-181.

Callan, T., B. Nolan, B.J. Whelan, C.T. Whelan, J. Williams (1996). *Poverty in the 90s: Evidence from the 1994 Living in Ireland Survey*, Dublin: Oak Tree Press.

Cameron, A., P. Trivedi, F. Milne and J. Piggott (1988). "A Microeconometric Model of the Demand for Health Care and Health Insurance in Australia." *Review of Economic Studies, LV,* 85-106.

Commission on Health Funding (1989), *Report*, Dublin: Stationery Office.

Department of Health (1994), "Shaping a Healthier Future: A Strategy for Effective Health Care in the 1990s," Dublin: Stationery Office

Harmon, C., R. Nestor and B. Nolan (1999). "Health Insurance and Health Services Utilisation in Ireland", Working Paper, The Economic and Social Research Institute.

Nolan, B. (1991). *The Utilization and Financing of Health Services in Ireland*, General Research Series No. 155, Dublin: The Economic and Social Research Institute.

Propper, C. (1989a). "Constrained Choice Sets in the UK Demand for Private Medical Insurance", *Journal of Public Economics*, Vol. 51, pp. 287-307.

Propper, C. (1989b). "An Econometric Analysis of the Demand for Private Health Insurance in England and Wales", *Applied Economics*, Vol. 21, pp. 777-792.

Propper, C. (1998). "Private Demand and Public Provision." Mimeo, University of Bristol.

Van de Ven, W. (1987). "An Econometric Model for the Simultaneous Estimation of the Demand for Medical Care and the Demand for Health Insurance," *Economics Letters*, Vol. 24, pp. 299-303.

Wiley, M. M. (1995), "Budgeting for Acute Hospital Services in Ireland: The Case-Mix Adjustment," *Journal of the Irish Colleges of Physicians and Surgeons*, Vol. 24, No. 4, October, pp. 283-90.